THE SPACE-FLIGHT
ENCYCLOPEDIA

THE SPACE-FLIGHT ENCYCLOPEDIA

Nicholas Roes &
William E. Kennedy

FOLLETT PUBLISHING COMPANY
Chicago • New York

Library of Congress Catalog Card Number; 68-18508

FIRST PRINTING I

T/8221

PREFACE

In his greatest series of adventures, man is exploring space by dispatching fiery vehicles up through the atmosphere to launch complex equipment. Sometimes man explores space only with instruments he has lofted on flight hardware—spacecraft or sounding rockets. At other times, he rides along to guide a spacecraft and gather knowledge with his own senses. Because man is vulnerable and not expendable, danger accompanies manned exploration in a hazardous environment filled with the unknown. Yet a sense of challenge exceeds the sense of danger. Man will not turn back. In unmanned and manned space exploration during the 1960's, he has opened immense new vistas in his quest for knowledge—vistas as limitless as the universe itself.

Pioneering has marked many steps along this journey to increased knowledge. In the comparatively early days of space exploration (1960), a Douglas Aircraft engineer, standing on Cape Canaveral's famed Pad 14, which was later to launch the Project Mercury astronauts, commented to one of this book's editors: "We couldn't go to a library and take the plans for a launching pad out of a book, because there wasn't a book on launching pads when we started. It took teamwork to figure out what to do."

During the 1960's the United States and the USSR have pursued prodigious space efforts, both military and peaceful. (General Bernard A. Schriever summed up the way the two purposes converge when he said: "The Air Force intercontinental ballistic missile development program has created much of the technology, hardware, and facilities that have been utilized in the nation's space program. Most of the nation's space shots to date have been launched by military boosters from Air Force facilities.") Today the new knowledge and experience of the two space leaders, and of other countries, too, lies within such diverse disciplines as astronautics, medicine, engineering, biology, chemistry, communications, data processing, mathematics, metallurgy, and propulsion. Acres of research and development laboratories and factories staffed with scientists and skilled workmen, and acres of launching facilities, support space exploration.

A National Aeronautics and Space Administration official, Dr. George E. Mueller, associate administrator for manned space flight, has identified "seven major elements in this space capability—people, industrial base, ground facilities, launch vehicles, spacecraft, operational know-how, and the ability to manage research and development. Together they add up to space power, which provides this country freedom of action in this new medium."

Although public attention has been focused on the glamorous goal of putting a man on the moon, NASA administrator James E. Webb has advocated that the emphasis be placed "where it really belongs: on the rapid growth of American competence in all areas of manned space flight, particularly in the area near earth which is the prime importance for national security."

The advancing space science and technology—American, Soviet, and other—deluges a student or an interested layman with a bewildering variety of terms, and unusual proper names for missions and equipment. In addition, some of the major events have become a blur in memory simply because of the rapidity of progress. To assist the student or interested layman beset by these problems, this book endeavors to compress an immense subject—space exploration—into a relatively small size. It is designed to serve as an easy-to-read guide to understanding terms, events, and concepts in man's exploration of space. We hope that it enables you to observe more intelligently and fruitfully as man reaches for new heights.

NICHOLAS ROES
WILLIAM E. KENNEDY

ACKNOWLEDGMENTS

The authors owe thanks to many individuals and organizations who have given generously of their time in the preparation of this book.

As might be expected, the "space agency"—the National Aeronautics and Space Administration—made available an abundance of information. George Gardner, educational publications officer in the Office of Public Affairs, and William J. O'Donnell, news chief in the Public Information Service, were particularly helpful.

For the United States Air Force, Col. James F. Reid, of the Office of Information in New York, supplied highly useful suggestions; and Headquarters, Air Force Systems Command, and Headquarters, Eastern Test Range, gave major aid.

To the Magazine and Book Branch, Directorate for Information Services, Department of Defense; the Aerospace Industries Association; American Institute of Aeronautics and Astronautics; and American Institute of Physics we also are indebted for assistance.

Corporate assistance came from the Boeing Company, Chrysler Corporation, Communications Satellite Corporation, Honeywell, Inc., International Business Machines Corporation, Lockheed Aircraft Corporation, McDonnell Douglas Corporation, Martin Marietta Corporation, North American Aviation, Inc., Radio Corporation of America, and TRW Systems, Inc.

ENTRIES OF SPECIAL INTEREST

A-1. An 88-pound satellite orbited by France, making that nation the third in the world to launch a satellite. The A-1 was boosted on Nov. 26, 1965, by a Diamant rocket from a French launching site in the Sahara Desert.

AAP. See *Apollo Applications Program.*

ablating material. A special material on the surface of a spacecraft that dissipates heat by melting or vaporizing. By sacrificing itself, an ablating material enables a spacecraft to re-enter the earth's atmosphere without being destroyed. In a complex process, an ablating material absorbs heat by increase in temperature and change in chemical or physical state. The heat is carried away from the surface by a loss of mass (liquid or vapor).

Phenolic nylon, a charring-ablation material, was given its first flight tests under actual re-entry conditions in 1966. The density of this plastic is low because millions of microscopic plastic spheres—called microballoons—are mixed in it. In general, charring ablator heat shields are covered with plastic resin materials reinforced with various organic or inorganic substances. See *heat shield.*

ablation. The erosion of heat-shield or nose-cone materials by melting or vaporizing during re-entry of spacecraft or missiles into the atmosphere. Re-entry speeds are hypersonic and produce high temperatures—up to 3,000° F on a Gemini manned spacecraft. The literal boiling away of the outer surface permits the inner part of the vehicle to remain relatively cool. See *heat shield.*

Able and **Baker.** Monkeys who participated in the first U.S. flight carrying animals into space for tests. On May 28, 1959, they were carried to an altitude of 350 miles on a Jupiter missile, which splashed down into the Atlantic 1,500 miles from Cape Kennedy (then Cape Canaveral).

abort. The premature termination of a flight because of a malfunction. An abort may occur during the countdown or during flight at any time before the destination is reached.

abort sequence. During manned flights in the Apollo program, a launch escape system can hurl the spacecraft and its three-man crew away from the Saturn launch vehicle to avoid a catastrophe. An abort via the launch escape system can be initiated any time between liftoff and 22 seconds after separation of the Saturn first stage. Beyond that point, the abort maneuver would be achieved by firing the main propulsion engine in the Apollo service module.

Launch escape system abort. If an Apollo crew initiates an abort at low altitude (0 to 12,000 feet), events are scheduled in the following sequence:

Abort plus 0 seconds—A solid-propellant motor ignites within the 33-foot-tall launch escape system and drives the spacecraft up and away from the Saturn.

Abort plus 11 seconds—Canards (two winglike surfaces near the top of the system) are deployed.

Abort plus 14 seconds—Launch escape system is jettisoned.

Abort plus 14.4 seconds—Forward heat shield is jettisoned.

Abort plus 16 seconds—Drogues (small conical parachutes) are deployed.

Abort plus 28 seconds—Drogues are released; pilot and main chutes are deployed.

Service module propulsion system abort. The Apollo command and service modules separate from the Saturn. The main propulsion engine in the service module burns for 10 seconds to propel the spacecraft away from the Saturn. Then the command module separates from the service module and re-enters the atmosphere in the usual way.

acceleration. The rate of change of velocity. Acceleration is usually measured in feet (or centimeters) per second per second. On earth, man experiences a rate of acceleration of 1g (the "g" refers to gravity; see *gravitation*). When riding in a spacecraft atop a rising launch vehicle, man experiences acceleration and requires special protection. Acceleration poses problems in space flight because there is a maximum acceleration beyond which man cannot survive. Yet, to put a spacecraft into the proper trajectory, the launch vehicle must be accelerated rapidly. A manned vehicle accelerates gradually at liftoff, reaches a maximum acceleration after it has passed through the atmosphere, and attains the desired velocity, when acceleration ends.

To protect astronauts, precautions must be taken. Best known are the contour couches in which the astronauts recline during accelerated flight. But perhaps more important is the control of the rate of acceleration, which keeps the "g-load" within the range of human endurance. In effect, rockets are not accelerated as rapidly as they could be—the rocket could stand it but man could not.

A decrease in acceleration is called negative acceleration, or deceleration. It is encountered by astronauts when their spacecraft re-enter the atmosphere or when retrorockets are fired to alter trajectory. (See *braking*.)

accelerometer. In space terminology, a device aboard a space vehicle for measuring acceleration (in any direction—roll, pitch, or yaw). Mounted on a stable platform that can level itself automatically and keep itself pointed in a fixed direction, accelerometers play essential roles in a vehicle guidance system.

Acceptance Checkout Equipment for Spacecraft (ACE/SC). Computers, display consoles, and recording equipment that provide an instantaneous method to verify the readiness of a spacecraft for flight. ACE/SC, manufactured by General Electric Co., was introduced in 1966 at the first flight of an unmanned Apollo spacecraft and will be used throughout the Apollo program. It also is used in the Manned Spacecraft Center, Houston, and in spacecraft-manufacturing plants.

access time. In computer operation, the time interval required to get information to or from the memory section.

acoustic grenade. A grenade ejected and detonated from a sounding rocket to assist in obtaining data at altitudes from 25 to 60 miles. The grenades are detonated at regular intervals during the rocket's ascent. NASA explains: "Average temperature and winds in the area between grenade detonations are obtained by measuring the exact time of detonation of each grenade, time of arrival of each sound wave at ground microphones, and the exact position of each detonation."

acquisition. "(1) The process of locating the orbit of a satellite or trajectory of a space probe so that tracking or telemetry data can be gathered. (2) The process of pointing an antenna or telescope so that it is properly oriented to allow gathering of tracking or telemetry data from a satellite or space probe."—(NASA)

Thus an 85-foot parabolic antenna at a tracking station at Fairbanks, Alaska, "acquires" the Nimbus 2 on ten of the spacecraft's fourteen daily orbits. And because the station obtains weather photographs from the satellite on its facsimile machine, it is called a "data acquisition facility."

acquisition lights. Powerful lights placed on a spacecraft to make it readily visible to another craft approaching for a rendezvous. In history's first space rendezvous, the Gemini 7 carried two lights, placed 180° apart, to assist the pilot of the approaching Gemini 6. The lights flashed eighty times a minute and were visible about twenty-three miles. The Agena target vehicle carried similar acquisition lights when overtaken by Gemini 8.

active communications satellite. An earth-circling satellite that receives a message from a ground-based transmitter and then actively transmits the message to a second ground station. Solar batteries on board the satellite supply power for receivers and transmitters. Telstar, launched in 1962, was a prototype; Early Bird, launched in 1965, became the first active communications satellite used commercially.

Aerobee. A family of sounding and research rockets built by Space-General Corp. A high-performance version first used for space research in 1966 is the Aerobee 350, which is 50 feet long, 22 inches in diameter, and weighs over 3.5 tons without payload. It is designed to boost a 500-pound payload to 210 miles or a 150-pound payload to 290 miles. The Aerobee 350's main stage consists of four liquid-fuel engines, each of which delivers 4,100 pounds of thrust at sea level and burns for 52 seconds. It also has a solid-fuel Nike booster, which delivers 52,000 pounds of thrust while burning for only 3.2 seconds. The main stage and booster fire almost simultaneously. The spent booster drops away, and the liquid-propulsion system—smoother than a solid-fuel system—gives a delicate scientific payload a "soft ride" to high altitudes.

aerodynamics. The branch of physics that treats of the motion of bodies relative to the air and the forces that act upon the bodies. The field includes such phenomena as shock waves and heat increases caused by friction and compression.

aeropause. The "region in which functional effects of the atmosphere on man and aircraft cease to exist."—(American, British, and Canadian Tripartite Air Forces)

aerospace. The earth's envelope of air, or atmosphere, and the space beyond it. The two realms are regarded as one for launching and navigating vehicles that travel in both. No sharply defined boundary exists between the atmosphere and space.

The U.S. Air Force, in its official standardized terms and definitions (Air Force Manual 11–1), calls aerospace "an operationally indivisible medium consisting of the total expanse beyond the earth's surface." It adds: "Space—the expanse (perhaps limitless) which surrounds the celestial bodies of the universe—cannot be precisely defined. The characteristics of various parts of space are different. For example, near earth, gas particles that form the 'air' or 'atmosphere' are close together and the earth's gravitational pull is comparatively strong. Elsewhere in space are other environments in which other forces and conditions exist. . . . Air and space form an indivisible operational medium, a continuum best described as aerospace."

For purposes of international law, Norman Sissenwine, U.S. Air Force Cambridge Research Laboratories scientist and co-chairman of the U.S. Committee on the Extension of the Standard Atmosphere, has suggested about sixty miles (one hundred kilometers) as the lowest altitude for an arbitrarily drawn demarcation line between air space and outer space. He noted that the atmosphere's basic composition begins to change at that point. In addition, he said, most meteor

trails—formed as meteors disintegrate in the atmosphere—
are observed below the fifty-mile mark. See *atmosphere*.

Aerospace Industries Association of America, Inc. The national
trade association of the manufacturers of aircraft, missiles,
spacecraft, propulsion, navigation and guidance systems,
support equipment, accessories, parts, materials, and components used in the construction, operation, and maintenance
of these aerospace products. Previously known as the Aircraft Industries Association of America, the association took
its present name in 1959 to reflect the industry's additional
efforts in missiles and space vehicles as well as its continuing
activities in aircraft design and production. Its headquarters
is 1725 De Sales Street, N.W., Washington, D.C. 20036.

AIA publishes annually *Aerospace Facts and Figures, Organization and Functions* and an *Annual Report,* and it
publishes monthly a magazine, *Aerospace.*

The membership of AIA includes sixty-one aerospace
manufacturing companies plus their corporate divisions. Together these companies employ more than one million persons. They produce about $19 billion in products and services
each year.

The AIA supports the National Aerospace Education
Council, 806 Fifteenth Street, N.W., Washington, which dis-
tributes educational materials concerning aerospace activities to schools and libraries throughout the country. These
materials include the annual *U.S. Aircraft, Missiles and
Spacecraft.*

aerothermodynamic border. "An altitude at about 100 miles,
above which the atmosphere is so rarefied that the motion of
an object through it at high speeds generates no significant
surface heat."—(NASA)

Aerodynamic forces therefore can generally be ignored in
flights above this border.

**Aerothermodynamic/elastic Structural Systems Environmental
Tests (ASSET).** A six-vehicle Air Force program from 1963
to 1965 to test a vehicle using the glide concept of re-entry,
to see how it fared in the "fireball" effect of returning to the
earth's atmosphere. In each demonstration an unmanned,
1,100-pound delta-winged glider rode on a Thor or Thor-

Delta launch vehicle on a nonorbital flight from Cape Kennedy. Then test vehicles were fired downward for a glide through the atmosphere. Skin temperatures as high as 4,000° F were encountered in a 1,650-mile glide. Five vehicles used zirconium-rod nose caps; the other had a coated tungsten nose cap. The Department of Defense followed up ASSET with a broader program called START to develop a manned lifting body vehicle. See *lifting body* and *Spacecraft Technology and Advanced Re-entry Test (START)*.

AFETR. See *Air Force Eastern Test Range*.

AFSC. See *Air Force Systems Command*.

afterburning. An irregular burning of left-over fuel in some rocket engines after the main burning and thrust have been stopped.

aft-firing thrusters. Maneuvering rockets aimed out of the tail of a spacecraft.

AFWTR. *See Air Force Western Test Range*.

Agena. A vehicle that has performed important assignments in space exploration by both NASA and the Department of Defense since 1959. The Agena helped propel Rangers to the moon and Mariners close to Venus and Mars, and served as the target vehicle in the first docking in space.

The Agena, which is 26 feet long and weighs less than a ton when empty, is an upper stage used with a Thor or an Atlas first stage. It may be employed in three ways: (1) to inject a spacecraft into earth orbit; (2) to become an earth-orbiting satellite itself, as it did as a docking target for Gemini 8; or (3) to restart while in earth orbit and launch an instrumented package deep into space. Payloads may exceed 2.5 tons.

Its builder, the Lockheed Missiles and Space Company, said of the agena: "It has telemetered more data from space than all other U.S. space vehicles combined. Agena was the world's first satellite to achieve circular orbit, first to make a polar orbit, first to be controlled in three axes during flight, first to provide restart capability [pump-fed engine]."

The Agena main engine may be restarted even after it has been idle in space for weeks. This is possible because its propellants are storable and hypergolic (ignite on contact).

These propellants are an oxidizer, IRFNA (inhibited red fuming nitric acid), and a fuel, UDMH (unsymmetrical dimethyl hydrazine).

Characteristics of a typical Agena vehicle:

Length: 26 ft.
Diameter: 5 ft.
Vehicle weight (empty): 1,484 lbs.
Propellant weight: 13,553 lbs.
Mixture ratio (oxidizer/fuel): 2.55
Thrust (vacuum): 16,140 lbs.
Burn time: 243 sec.

Agena Target Vehicle. The standard Air Force Agena (D model) was modified by the Space Systems Command of the Air Force Systems Command to serve as a rendezvous spacecraft in Project Gemini.

Operating as a separate second stage of an Atlas-Agena vehicle, the Agena put itself into orbit with its own Bell Aerosystems main propulsion engine of 16,000 pounds of thrust. In orbit, the Agena was maneuvered both by ground control and by the Gemini 8 crew. Its main engine could be restarted to make large orbital changes. Small velocity changes were made by two aft-firing, 200-pound thrust engines. In addition, two other aft-firing, 16-pound thrust engines made vernier adjustments. Six nitrogen jets mounted on the Agena aft end controlled roll, pitch, and yaw. The Agena lifted off as a 36.3-foot-long vehicle but jettisoned a 7.3-foot shroud and adapter. Loaded with fuel, it orbited at a weight of 7,000 pounds. See *Augmented Target Docking Adapter*.

AIAA. See *American Institute of Aeronautics and Astronautics*.

AIMP. Anchored Interplanetary Monitoring Platform. See *Explorer*.

air. See *aerospace* and *atmosphere*.

Air Force Eastern Test Range (AFETR). A 10,000-mile-long range—the world's largest outdoor laboratory—extending from Patrick Air Force Base, Fla., down the South Atlantic Ocean and into the Indian Ocean. It is part of the National Range Division established in mid-1964 under the Air Force

Systems Command. The AFETR was formerly known as the Atlantic Missile Range; its counterpart in the NRD is the Air Force Western Test Range, which up to mid-1964 was known as the Pacific Missile Range.

When a space vehicle or a military missile is launched from Cape Kennedy, the AFETR calls into action sophisticated instrumentation at island stations—such as Grand Bahama, Eleuthera, Antigua, and Ascension—and on ships and aircraft.

Equipment includes such specialized installations as a diesel-powered generating plant that eliminates dependence on distant commercial sources for critical electricity for launches, and giant pumping systems that deliver high-pressure water to cool the launch pads.

Air Force Systems Command (AFSC). The AFSC advances technology in spacecraft, as well as in missiles and aircraft, and adapts the technology into operational systems. The command was established in April 1961 to provide the most effective management of Air Force scientific and technical resources.

The AFSC manages more than $3 billion worth of aerospace facilities at three hundred sites in the U.S. and around the world. Its installations include five development and test centers. In addition, the command directs the spending of about one-third of the Air Force budget and administers more than five thousand contracts in a military-industrial-scientific partnership.

The AFSC carries out the major space responsibilities of the Department of Defense (DOD). Under agreements between DOD and NASA, this Air Force command provides research, development, test, and engineering of boosters, spacecraft, and associated systems to support specific NASA programs and projects. Thus, in Project Gemini manned launches, the AFSC has provided men and facilities through its National Range Division and Space Systems Division.

On the leading edge of technology, the Air Force has developed a series of missiles that later became launch vehicles (up to the size of the giant three-barreled Titan 3-C), and is developing a space station to be known as the Manned Orbiting Laboratory.

AIR FORCE SYSTEMS COMMAND
Headquarters
Andrews AFB (Air Force Base), Washington, D.C.

DIVISIONS

Space and Missile Systems Organization (SAMSO), Los Angeles Air Force Station, Cal.

National Range Division, Andrews AFB, Washington, D.C.
Foreign Technology Division, Wright-Patterson AFB, Ohio
Aeronautical Systems Division, Wright-Patterson AFB, Ohio
Research and Technology Division, Bolling AFB, Washington, D.C.

Aerospace Medical Division, Brooks AFB, Texas

Electronic Systems Division, L. G. Hanscom Field, Mass.

Air Force Contract Management Division, Air Force Unit Post Office, Los Angeles

CENTERS

Air Force Flight Test Center, Edwards AFB, Cal.

Arnold Engineering Development Center, Arnold Air Force Station, Tenn.

Air Force Missile Development Center, Holloman AFB, N.M.

Air Proving Ground Center, Eglin AFB, Fla.

Air Force Special Weapons Center, Kirkland AFB, N.M.

RANGES

Air Force Eastern Test Range, Patrick AFB, Fla.

Air Force Western Test Range, Vandenberg AFB, Cal.

Air Force Western Test Range (AFWTR). Launching facilities at Vandenberg Air Force Base along the Pacific Ocean in California, together with facilities for tracking space vehicles and missiles out into the Pacific Ocean past Hawaii and Eniwetok.

The Air Force operates the AFWTR as part of its National Range Division (together with the Air Force Eastern Test Range at Cape Kennedy).

The AFWTR launching area juts out into the ocean midway between Los Angeles and San Francisco and is well situated for launches into polar orbits (toward the South Pole and then over the North Pole). Nimbus and other unmanned spacecraft flying pole-to-pole orbits look down eventually on all parts of the earth as it turns beneath them.

The AFWTR is also capable of launching sounding rockets and deep-space probes and will have manned missions when the Defense Department's Manned Orbiting Laboratory is launched from there.

airglow. A relatively steady glow in the night sky. It is caused by release in the upper atmosphere of energy absorbed from the sun during daylight. In contrast, the aurora borealis—or northern lights—glow sporadically.

Data on differences between airglow and the aurora were gathered by a Rice University team of experimenters in 1964, using sounding rockets supplied by NASA. The Rice group fired rockets from Fort Churchill, Canada, into the polar aurora, analyzed the information, and reported that the aurora originated when electron particles from space bombarded oxygen and nitrogen atoms in the upper atmosphere. However, in tests of airglow with rockets launched in Virginia (from Wallops Island), the researchers found too few high-atmosphere particles present to account for airglow by electron bombardment. Identification and measurement of particles was accomplished with a magnetic mass spectrometer.

albedo. Reflective power, as of the moon, a planet, or an artificial satellite. Albedo, usually expressed as a percentage, is the ratio of the amount of electro-magnetic radiation reflected by a body to the amount falling on it. For a completely black body, the albedo is 0.0; for a completely white body, it is 1.0. The angle of incidence of an incoming light may change the albedo of a surface. Satellites are often given bright surfaces to increase the albedo and make visual tracking easier.

Alouette. A Canadian "topside sounder" satellite. Alouette 1 was launched by a United States booster in 1962. The 320-pound, nearly oval Alouette circled the earth from 620 to 640 miles high, above (or topside of) the region of the greatest electron density. "Sweeping" over a wide range of frequencies, the satellite used a radio-echo sounding technique to gather data, by latitude, on daily and seasonal fluctuations in electron density. Previously, such data—important to radio communications—were gathered only by "bottomside sounding" from ground stations. The Alouette also returned data on galactic noise and cosmic rays. All design, development, and construction on the satellite was done in Canada. That country's second satellite, Alouette 2, was launched in 1965 along with U.S. Explorer 31, by a single rocket, to study the ionosphere in the polar regions.

ALSEP. See *Apollo Lunar Surface Experiments Package.*

altitudes. NASA customarily gives orbital measurements in statute miles. For nautical miles, multiply by .87. For kilometers multiply by 1.61.

American Institute of Aeronautics and Astronautics (AIAA). A 36,000-member society devoted to the advancement of the arts, sciences, and technology of aeronautics and astronautics. About 60 per cent of AIAA's members are engaged in engineering or research, 30 per cent in technical management, and 10 per cent in corporate management. A nonprofit membership society, AIAA was formed in 1963 by the merger of the American Rocket Society (founded 1930) and the Institute of the Aerospace Sciences (founded 1932). Its headquarters are at 1290 Avenue of the Americas, New York City.

The AIAA's largest operation is the Technical Information Service, which, through a contract with NASA, provides extracts of current published technical literature. The institute publishes *Astronautics and Aeronautics,* a general engineering magazine; the *AIAA Journal,* a research and development journal; the *Journal of Spacecraft and Rockets;* the *Journal of Aircraft;* and the *AIAA Bulletin.*

Ames Research Center. A NASA installation at Moffett Field, Cal., near Mountain View and San Francisco. To advance both space technology and aeronautics, the Ames Research Center conducts basic and applied research in physical and life science areas. For example, Ames researchers explored aerodynamic shapes to find the best ones for spacecraft of the future. Facilities include a $10 million Advanced Flight Simulation Laboratory with a $50g$ man-carrying motion generator, or centrifuge.

AMU. See *astronaut maneuvering unit.*

anacoustic zone. The zone of silence in space. The Air Force defines it as "the region above 100 miles altitude where the distance between the rarefied air molecules is greater than the wave length of sound, and sound waves can no longer be propagated."

analog computer. A computing machine that works on the principle of measuring, in contrast to a digital computer, which counts. Input data may include light intensities, linear lengths, and voltages.

Anchored Interplanetary Monitoring Platform (AIMP). See *Explorer.*

angstrom. A unit of length used to measure light waves. Ten billion angstroms equal one meter.

ANNA 1B (for Army, Navy, NASA, and Air Force). A 350-pound satellite for measuring the size and shape of the earth. Launched in 1962, ANNA 1B conducted its geodetic studies with the aid of a powerful flashing beacon and radio signals relayed to earth on command. The Johns Hopkins University Applied Physics Laboratory built the satellite.

antennas. Large "dish" antennas are parabolic reflectors used by NASA for tracking and telemetry. They locate a spacecraft, follow its course, determine its velocity, direction, orbital eccentricity, and period of orbit, and communicate with it. Because NASA's antennas must track and communicate across the sky from horizon to horizon, most of them are fully steerable to assure maneuverability and flexibility.

In contrast, many other large antennas around the world are designed for radio astronomy and do not require such maneuverability. Often they fix on a single star or galaxy.

NASA's very large, fully steerable antennas are:

210-foot in diameter—Goldstone, Cal.—for missions to the moon and planets.

85-foot in diameter—Goldstone, Cal., and Fairbanks, Alas.; Rosman, N.C.; Spain, South Africa, and Australia—for deep space, Apollo missions, and weather and scientific satellites.

The United States has five other large antennas, as follows:

150-foot in diameter (fully steerable)—Air Force Cambridge Research Laboratory, Sagamore Hill Radio Observatory, Hamilton, Mass.—for radio communications and astronomy.

140-foot in diameter (fully steerable)—National Science Foundation, Greenbank, W. Va.—for radio astronomy.

120-foot in diameter (fully steerable) radar-radio telescope—Air Force, operated by Lincoln Laboratory, Massachusetts Institute of Technology, Haystack Hill, Tyngsboro, Mass.—for radio communications research and astronomy.

300-foot diameter (partially steerable)—National Science Foundation, Greenbank, W. Va., a single-axis antenna, like a transit—for astronomy.

1,000-foot in diameter (nonsteerable)—Department of Defense, Advanced Research Projects Agency, Arecibo Ionospheric Observatory, Puerto Rico—a radar-radio telescope for astronomy.

See *Goldstone "210"* and *Jodrell Bank.*

Spacecraft antenna, used to radiate and receive radio waves, come in a great variety of forms. In the Gemini manned flights, several different antennas were used—high-frequency whip, ultra-high-frequency whip, C-band helical, C-band slot, descent, recovery, and UHF nose stub.

aphelion. The point farthest from the sun in a planet's elliptical (oval) orbit around the sun. The earth's aphelion is about 94.5 million miles from the sun in July. The earth's perihelion —the point nearest the sun—is about 91.5 million miles from the sun in January.

apogee. The point farthest from the earth in the elliptical orbit around the earth. The first Gemini manned spacecraft had an apogee of 204 miles. In each orbit it dropped to a low point—or perigee—of 99.6 miles.

apogee motor or **apogee "kick rocket."** A small motor that is fired when a spacecraft reaches the farthest distance from earth in an elliptical orbit. An apogee motor was first used on Syncom 2 in 1963 to apply enough power to change its trajectory and "kick" it up to a synchronous-orbit altitude of about 22,300 miles.

Apollo (project). A NASA project, centered on a three-man spacecraft, to land two American explorers on the moon and bring them back safely. Project Apollo is the largest single scientific and engineering job of all time. President John F. Kennedy made a manned lunar landing a national goal when he said to Congress on May 25, 1961: "I believe this nation should commit itself to achieving the goal, before this decade is out, of landing a man on the moon and returning him safely

The Apollo spacecraft being raised up the gantry for mating to the Saturn booster.

to earth." The national program eventually involved more than twenty thousand companies. At about the midway point in the 1960's, costs were estimated as likely to reach $22.7 billion by completion of the program in 1970. (The cost estimate included Projects Mercury and Gemini as necessary preliminaries to Apollo.)

About 90 per cent of the predicted cost was attributed to the building of an over-all space-flying capability, rather than to the lunar voyage itself. The cost of building the over-all capability included ground facilities, launch vehicles and spacecraft, astronaut training, management, and so on.

What It Is. Possibly the quickest grasp of Project Apollo

may be had by thinking of sets of threes: three astronauts, three-part Apollo spacecraft, three-stage Saturn launch vehicle, and three-stage mission (voyage to the moon, exploration of the moon in a lunar module, and return voyage to the earth).

Sometimes the venture is referred to as Apollo/Saturn, from the names of the spacecraft and the launch vehicle.

Spacecraft. The Apollo spacecraft assembly, including its rocket-powered escape tower, stands eighty-two feet tall—almost as tall as the 1963 Mercury spacecraft and its Atlas launch vehicle combined. The parts of the spacecraft are:

1. Command module. This control center will house a three-man crew, and computer and other instruments, within a blunt, cone-shaped body 12 feet high and 13 feet in diameter at its base. Environment control will enable the crew to live in the module without wearing pressure suits. Life support will be sufficient for a fourteen-day mission—a capability demonstrated by the Gemini 7 mission. The 12,000-pound Apollo command module, made of honeycomb steel, is the only piece of hardware that will return to earth. Therefore it is designed with an epoxy-resin heat shield to withstand the fireball effect encountered when re-entering the atmosphere at 25,000 mph.

2. Service module. This section contains a 21,500-pound-thrust rocket engine to propel the craft on its way to and from the moon, to provide braking for the lunar orbit, and to permit other operations in space. The service module also contains hydrogen-oxygen fuel cells to provide electrical power, advanced radar, and radiators for space cooling. It is cylindrical in shape, 22 feet high including the engine skirt, 13 feet in diameter, and weighs 55,000 pounds when fueled. The service module will be jettisoned immediately before the spacecraft re-enters the atmosphere. North American Rockwell builds both the command and the service modules and also the launch escape system.

3. Lunar module. This module is a 31,700-pound space ferry with four spidery legs for support when landing on the moon. About 20 feet high and 30 feet in diameter including its extended landing gear, it will transport two astronauts from the orbiting Apollo spacecraft down to the moon, firing retro-rockets to assure a soft landing. Using its ascent engine

on liftoff from the moon, it will leave its descent engine and legs behind. After it docks with the spacecraft to permit its two-man crew to re-enter the command module, the lunar module will be jettisoned in lunar orbit. Grumman Aircraft Engineering Corp. builds the lunar module.

Launch Vehicle. Saturn 5, when assembled ready to lift off into space, stands 363 feet tall, the equivalent of a thirty-six-story building. It measures thirty-three feet in diameter at its base. Saturn 5's three stages generate 8.7 million pounds of thrust—fourteen times more than the Titan 2, the launch vehicle that put the Gemini spacecraft into orbit. The stages of Saturn 5 are:

First stage (Boeing Company). Five North American Rockwell Rocketdyne F-1 engines generate 7.5 million pounds of thrust—equivalent to 160 million horsepower, or the power of roughly 600,000 automobiles. The engines lift the 3,000-ton launch vehicle to an altitude of thirty miles before the stage drops away.

Second stage (North American Rockwell). Five Rocketdyne J-2 engines supply 1,000,000 pounds of total thrust and push the spacecraft to a 100-mile orbital altitude.

Third stage (McDonnell Douglas). One J-2 engine supplies 200,000 pounds of thrust to put the spacecraft into earth orbit. Later the engine is restarted at the proper time and position to direct the spacecraft toward the moon at nearly 25,000 mph.

NASA's Manned Spacecraft Center is responsible for the design and development of the spacecraft, and NASA's Marshall Space Flight Center is responsible for the design and development of the launch vehicle. Contractors in addition to those named for stages and engines include: Avco's Research and Development Division, ablative heat shield; Collins Radio, communications and data; Control Data, digital test command system; Garrett AiResearch, environmental control; General Motors' AC Spark Plug Division, inertial guidance; Honeywell, stabilization and control; Marquardt Corp., service module reaction control motors; Massachusetts Institute of Technology Instrumentation Laboratory, guidance and navigation; Raytheon, on-board digital computer; United Aircraft's Pratt & Whitney Division, fuel cell.

To the Moon and Back. Development of the gigantic Saturn 5 opened the way for a manned journey to the moon. A brief outline of that venture follows.

Voyage to Lunar Orbit. All the burning time of the Saturn 5's first two stages, and part of the third stage, are required to hurl the Apollo spacecraft into earth orbit. Then the third stage is fired a second time to push the craft out of the earth's gravitational field. The astronauts will separate the parent craft (command and service modules) from the lunar module and make a free fly-around—in effect a half circle—to connect the command module nose-to-nose with the exploration vehicle. The burned-out third stage of the Saturn will be jettisoned. Approaching the moon, the crewmen will rotate the Apollo to a tail-forward position and fire the rocket engine in the service module to enter a circular orbit eighty miles above the moon.

Travel by Space Ferry. Two crewmen will enter the lunar module, detach it, and guide it to a soft landing on the moon. They will be aided by an engine (TRW Systems) that can be throttled down from 10,500 pounds of thrust to one tenth of that thrust. After making scientific observations, collecting samples, and taking photographs, the two explorers will lift off in their lunar module, using the expended descent stage as a platform. The ascent engine (Bell Aerosystems) gives 3,500 pounds of thrust to carry the lunar module to a rendezvous and docking maneuver with the parent craft, which will have continued to orbit the moon with the third astronaut at the controls. After the two astronauts return to the Apollo through a tunnel, they will jettison the lunar module, leaving it in orbit around the moon.

Voyage Back to Earth. Restarting of the rocket engine in the service module will boost the Apollo out of the lunar orbit at 5,500 mph. Velocity will increase to 25,000 mph because of the effect of gravity as the spacecraft returns to earth. Operation of the rocket power will enable the astronauts to steer a precise course into the entry corridor, or entry window, that leads back to earth. Just before re-entry into the atmosphere, the service module will be jettisoned. The command module will be turned around so that the base shield dissipates the searing heat. Before the landing, a drogue parachute and three main parachutes will deploy to bring the command module down safely.

Early Steps to the Moon. Before it could go for the moon, the United States had to develop a launch vehicle with enough thrust to place more than forty-five tons into a lunar trajectory. The bigger vehicle was developed in steps—Saturn 1, Uprated Saturn 1, and Saturn 5.

Saturn 1 achieved 100 per cent success in ten launches from 1961 through 1965, when the program was closed out. A two-stage vehicle delivering a total of 1,590,000 pounds of thrust in 1965, Saturn 1 supplied valuable lessons in technology and methods of space exploration. Possibly the biggest single benefit was the experience gained in clustering eight large engines in the first stage. Launches included three Pegasus meteoroid technology satellites and unmanned Apollo command and service module "boilerplate" spacecraft (engineering test models). Saturn 1's heaviest payload was 39,200 pounds, placed in earth orbit in 1964.

Uprated Saturn 1, formerly designated the Saturn 1B, emerged in 1966 as an improved vehicle incorporating principles and hardware proved by Saturn 1. The 1B was created from the first stage of Saturn 1 and the third stage of the future Saturn 5 and delivered a combined thrust of 1.8 million pounds. It launched unmanned Apollo spacecraft into earth orbit to prove airworthiness and later will launch Apollo spacecraft carrying astronauts into earth orbits so that they can practice maneuvers essential to a lunar journey. For details of the engines, see *Saturn (launch vehicle).*

Purpose. Why put men on the moon? And is the moon landing in itself the foremost goal?

Reaching the moon, the celestial body nearest earth, is obviously the first step if man is to answer the challenge of journeying to other planetary bodies. Thus a lunar journey gives the United States space program a meaningful focus. But the larger goal in the man-on-the-moon project is the development of broad scientific and technological competence in the manned exploration of space.

The over-all objective was pinpointed by Dr. George E. Mueller, NASA associate administrator for manned space flight, when he said: "The facilities, manpower, flight hardware, and experience being created in the Apollo program will serve the country long after the program has been completed. In fact, fully 90 per cent of the work now in progress in Apollo would be done to create space power even if there were no moon and our efforts in manned space flight had an entirely different goal."

Only about 10 per cent of the total outlay represents "the extra cost of the lunar mission," NASA administrator James E. Webb pointed out. He added: "Let us all endeavor to put the emphasis where it really belongs: on the rapid growth of American competence in all areas of manned space flight, particularly in the area near earth which is the prime importance for national security."

Many of the skills developed for peaceful flight to the moon are also useful militarily.

Gen. Bernard A. Schriever, former chief of the Air Force Systems Command, said: "The nation that first achieves the ability to maneuver, to communicate, and to carry out military missions in and from space will enjoy a strategic advantage that could be decisive if not effectively countered."

A round trip to the moon clearly would demonstrate operational know-how in space. To achieve this feat, the United States is developing the other major elements of space power named by Dr. Mueller—trained people, industrial base, ground facilities, launch vehicles, spacecraft, and experience in managing research and development.

Apollo 204 Fire. This flash fire killed Virgil I. Grissom, Edward H. White, II, and Roger B. Chaffee as they conducted a ground test in an Apollo command module at Launch Complex 34, Cape Kennedy, on Jan. 27, 1967. The astronauts had been scheduled for launch on Feb. 21, 1967, in the first earth-orbital flight of the Apollo spacecraft and command modules (in what would have been Apollo/Saturn 204).

The eight-man Apollo 204 Review Board later found that "no single source of the fire was conclusively identified." The board determined that the test conditions were "extremely hazardous" after finding that: "(a) The command module contained many types and classes of combustible material in areas contiguous to possible ignition sources. (b) The test was conducted with 16.7 pounds per square inch absolute, 100 per cent oxygen atmosphere."

As an aftermath, the amount and location of combustible

materials was severely restricted and controlled, and the hatch, or door, was redesigned for quick exit.

Apollo Flight Schedule. NASA identifies its Apollo flights as either in the "200" series (Apollo spacecraft and Uprated Saturn rocket) or in the "500" series (Apollo spacecraft and Saturn 5 rocket).

NASA scheduled its 1968 Apollo missions in the following sequence:

AS-204: First unmanned test of lunar module in earth orbit.

AS-502: Second unmanned flight test of Saturn 5 launch vehicle and the Apollo command and service module. (For details of first flight on Nov. 7, 1967, and second flight on April 4, 1968, see *Saturn 5.*)

AS-503: Third unmanned test of Saturn 5 and command and service module.

AS-206: Second unmanned test of lunar module in earth orbit.

AS-205: First Apollo manned flight, a 10-day flight to qualify the command and service modules as airworthy for more manned missions.

AS-504: First manned Apollo flight on the Saturn 5 rocket; this mission to provide the first manned operation in space of the command and service module with the lunar module, so that two astronauts can transfer to the lunar module and practice rendezvous and docking.

For 1969 NASA scheduled AS-505, AS-506, AS-507, AS-508, and AS-509 as lunar mission development flights or lunar mission simulations. Six Saturn flights remain beyond that point. The first moon landing, NASA said, could come at AS-509 or later.

Apollo Applications Program (AAP). A program to follow the man-on-the-moon project by using its technology, Apollo spacecraft, and Saturn launch vehicles to extend man's ability to explore space.

Proposed missions include moon orbits to collect scientific information with cameras and sensors, and moon landings for extensive exploration of the surface. In addition, some proposed AAP missions would orbit the earth to conduct scientific, biomedical, technological, and operational experi-

asteroid (or planetoid or minor planet). A small starlike body orbiting around the sun. An asteroid may be a fragment of a broken planet. Some asteroids measure less than a mile in diameter; the largest, Ceres, is estimated at about 485 miles in diameter. Most asteroids are found between Mars and Jupiter, where they may present a hazard to space travel. "Far-out" talk in the 1960's produced the suggestion that man capture an asteroid and, using a nuclear-propulsion vehicle, bring it back into earth orbit for analysis.

astrodynamics. The planning and directing of the trajectories of space vehicles through application of celestial mechanics and allied fields. The scope of astrodynamics, as defined by the American Institute of Aeronautics and Astronautics, is: "The determination, improvement, prediction and physical adjustment of trajectories in space; space navigation and rendezvous; re-entry trajectories, attitude optimization; perturbation theories and expansions; differential correction and statistical processes; and observation reduction."

astronaut. The term, in the United States, for a person who engages in space flights. The USSR prefers "cosmonaut" for its space navigators.

By 1967 NASA had assembled a team of fifty-six astronauts, accepted in six groups beginning in 1959. The men selected in 1966 were required to have a bachelor's degree in engineering or physical or biological sciences. They also had to have acquired 1,000 hours of jet pilot time or to have graduated from an armed forces test pilot school. They could be no taller than six feet and no older than thirty-six upon the start of their astronaut duty. Most astronauts are members of the armed forces, but some are civilians.

A comparison of the first five astronaut groups at time of selection:

Group	Age	Years in College	Flight Hours
1959	34.5	4.3	3,500
1962	32.5	4.6	2,800
1963	30.0	5.6	2,315
1965	31.2	8.0	*
1966	32.8	5.8	2,714

* Scientist-astronaut group in which no pilot experience was required for selection.

The National Academy of Sciences joined with NASA in seeking out young (up to age thirty-six) scientists, medical doctors, and engineers to become astronauts in 1967 to explore space firsthand. A doctorate in the natural sciences, medicine, or engineering was required for entry into a group that would "conduct scientific experiments in manned orbiting satellites and observe and investigate the lunar surface and circumterrestrial space."

The USSR sent one woman cosmonaut, Valentina V. Tereshkova (who took the code name Seagull) on an earth-orbiting flight in 1963, but the United States has no woman astronauts. Physiologically, women would make excellent astronauts, a NASA medical official has said. However, they lack experience in flying high-speed aircraft or in handling the complex equipment used in space programs. Eleven men were accepted in the 1967 group; all were civilians.

In addition, U.S. military pilots were being trained for future space flight in the Department of Defense Manned Orbiting Laboratory. The acceptance of four pilots in 1967 brought their number up to 16.

At the end of 1967, there had been ten losses of astronauts among the 66 selected for the program. Two (including John H. Glenn) resigned and one (M. Scott Carpenter) returned to the U.S. Navy at the Navy's request to take part in the Deep Submergence Systems Project. Seven died—one in an automobile accident, three in a pair of jet crashes, and three in the Apollo 204 spacecraft fire.

The first Soviet Cosmonaut reported killed was Vladimir M. Komarov, whose Soyuz 1 spaceship plunged to earth on Apr. 24, 1967. Then on Mar. 27, 1968, Yuri A. Gagarin was killed in the crash of a jet plane about fifty miles from Moscow.

THE FIRST SPACEMEN AND SPACEWOMAN

Name and Country	Launch Date
1. Yuri A. Gagarin (USSR)	Apr. 12, 1961
2. Alan B. Shepard, Jr. (U.S.)	May 5, 1961
3. Virgil I. Grissom (U.S.)	July 21, 1961
4. Gherman S. Titov (USSR)	Aug. 6, 1961
5. John H. Glenn, Jr. (U.S.)	Feb. 20, 1962

6. M. Scott Carpenter (U.S.)	May 24, 1962
7. Andrian G. Nikolayev (USSR)	Aug. 11, 1962
8. Pavel R. Popovich (USSR)	Aug. 12, 1962
9. Walter M. Schirra, Jr. (U.S.)	Oct. 3, 1962
10. L. Gordon Cooper, Jr. (U.S.)	May 15, 1963
11. Valeri F. Bykovski (USSR)	June 14, 1962
12. Valentina V. Tereshkova (USSR)	June 16, 1963

{ 13. Vladimir M. Komarov, commander (USSR)   Oct. 12, 1964
{ 14. Konstantin P. Feoktistov (USSR)
{ 15. Dr. Boris B. Yegorov (USSR)

{ 16. Pavel Belyayev, commander (USSR)   Mar. 18, 1965
{ 17. Aleksei Leonov (USSR)

{ — Grissom (2d flight), commander (U.S.)   Mar. 23, 1965
{ 18. John W. Young (U.S.)

{ 19. James A. McDivitt, commander (U.S.)   June 3, 1965
{ 20. Edward H. White, II (U.S.)

{ — Cooper (2d flight), commander (U.S.)   Aug. 21, 1965
{ 21. Charles Conrad, Jr. (U.S.)

{ 22. Frank Borman, commander (U.S.)   Dec. 4, 1965
{ 23. James A. Lovell, Jr. (U.S.)

{ — Schirra (2d flight), commander (U.S.)   Dec. 15, 1965
{ 24. Thomas P. Stafford (U.S.)

{ 25. Neil A. Armstrong, commander (U.S.)   Mar. 16, 1966
{ 26. David R. Scott (U.S.)

{ — Stafford (2d flight), commander (U.S.)   June 3, 1966
{ 27. Eugene A. Cernan (U.S.)

{ — Young (2d flight), commander (U.S.)   July 18, 1966
{ 28. Michael Collins (U.S.)

{ — Conrad (2d flight), commander (U.S.)   Sept. 12, 1966
{ 29. Richard F. Gordon, Jr. (U.S.)

{ — Lovell (2d flight), commander (U.S.)   Nov. 11, 1966
{ 30. Edwin E. Aldrin, Jr. (U.S.)

— Komarov (2d flight, USSR)   Apr. 23, 1967

astronaut maneuvering unit (AMU). A backpack with a propulsion unit and oxygen supply to enable an astronaut to move about outside his vehicle in space.

When an astronaut first straps the pack on for a space walk, it weighs 166 pounds, including 24 pounds of hydrogen peroxide fuel and 7.5 pounds of oxygen. The rectangular aluminum pack—32 inches high, 22 inches wide, and 19 inches deep—contains a form-fitting cradle in which the astronaut is seated in flight. Twelve small thrusters mounted on the corners of the pack provide propulsion in all directions —four forward, four aft, two up, and two down. Each thruster delivers 2.3 pounds of thrust. The astronaut controls the firing through two sidearm supports attached to the backpack structure and communicates with the spacecraft with a battery-powered ultra-high frequency transceiver mounted on the backpack.

Four green running lights on the pack make the extra-vehicular astronaut readily visible to the crew member in the spacecraft. Throughout extravehicular maneuvering, the astronaut remains attached to the spacecraft with a 125-foot tether.

astronautics. "1. The art, skill, or activity of operating space-craft. 2. In a broader sense, the science of space flight."—(NASA)

The broad program areas used by NASA in managing the U.S. astronautics program are: manned space flight, space science and applications, advanced research and technology, and tracking and data acquisition.

astronomical unit (a.u.) The mean distance from the earth to the sun, or about 92.9 million miles. Astronomers use this unit—much more convenient than miles—to measure the vast distances in space. The mean distance from the sun of Pluto, outermost of the planets in the solar system, is 39.5 a.u.

ATDA. See *Augmented Target Docking Adapter*.

Atlantic Missile Range. See *Air Force Eastern Test Range*.

Atlas. Designed originally as an intercontinental ballistic missile for the Air Force, the Atlas has changed assignments over the years and become a space booster for a variety of NASA and military programs. After refinements from its version as a weapon, the rocket is known as the Atlas SLV-3 Standard Launch Vehicle.

In well over two hundred launches, the Atlas has built up a long string of successes in putting payloads of varying sizes into orbit. It has launched manned Mercury orbital flights (Glenn, Carpenter, Schirra, and Cooper); Agena target vehicles in Project Gemini; instrumented spacecraft such as

GENERAL DYNAMICS/CONVAIR

The Atlas-Agena launch vehicle with the Mariner spacecraft.

the Orbiting Geophysical Observatory for earth orbits; classified military missions; a Centaur upper stage designed for
Surveyor and other missions, and Ranger and Mariner shots
to the moon, Mars, and Venus. The Atlas may be launched
without an upper stage or in combination with either the
Agena or a Centaur as a second stage.

Standing almost seven stories tall without payload, the
Atlas is a 1½-stage vehicle (but the "half" designation is
dropped when referring to an Atlas-Agena or an Atlas-
Centaur). On the pad, the Atlas ignites all three main engines
as well as two small vernier engines. In ascent, the Atlas drops
off the half-stage, or two outboard booster engines (supplying
330,000 pounds of thrust). It continues firing its single sustainer or center engine (57,000 pounds of thrust). In addition, the two vernier engines (each with 1,500 pounds of

thrust) provide balance for trajectory and final velocity control. In an Atlas launch sequence, there are three commands to shut down engines: booster engine cutoff (BECO), sustainer engine cutoff (SECO), and vernier engine cutoff (VECO).

The Convair Division of General Dynamics, principal contractor for Atlas, builds the airframe and integrates the systems. Standardized guidance, autopilot, tracking, telemetry, and electrical system kits are installed to tailor each vehicle to its launch site and specific mission. Separate tracking kits, for example, are kept in readiness for flights on the Western Test Range and the Eastern Test Range.

The Rocketdyne Division of North American Rockwell Corp. builds the engines and General Electric Co. provides guidance. Over-all management of the Atlas vehicle program is handled by the Space Systems Division of the Air Force Systems Command.

Salient facts about the Atlas Standard Launch Vehicle:

Height: 66 ft.

Diameter: lower booster section, 16 ft.; tank section, 10 ft.;
tapered nose section, 5 ft. 10 in.

Weight (fully fueled): 260,000 lbs.

Oxidizer (upper tank): liquid oxygen

Fuel (lower tank): RF-1

Propellant consumption rate: about 1,500 lbs. per sec.

Burn time: about 5 min.

Atlas-Agena. A two-stage vehicle that gained prominence in Project Gemini when the second stage went into earth orbit as a target vehicle in rendezvous maneuvers. See *Agena, Agena Target Vehicle,* and *Atlas.*

Atlas-Centaur. A combination of a modified Atlas missile with a Centaur upper stage, creating a 113-foot vehicle and weighing 151 tons at liftoff. When used with Centaur, the tapered nose of the Atlas is enlarged so that the entire vehicle has a constant 10-foot diameter. See *Atlas* and *Centaur.*

Atomic Energy Commission (AEC). The federal commission that administers the nation's atomic energy program. The AEC's research and development will play an important part in providing power for prolonged space flights in the future.

Working jointly with NASA in Project Rover, the AEC seeks to develop nuclear-powered engines for space propulsion. One class of engines would supply a large thrust for a short time in a launch vehicle; a second class of engines would supply a small thrust for a long time in a craft traveling through space.

Working with the Defense Department and NASA in Project SNAP (Systems for Nuclear Auxiliary Power), the AEC seeks to develop spacecraft on-board power for data transmission, communications, and other purposes. See *Rover* and *Systems for Nuclear Auxiliary Power.*

atmosphere. A mixture of gases surrounding the earth and other heavenly bodies. The earth's atmospheric pressure is greatest at lower levels and decreases at higher altitudes. About 99 per cent of its atmosphere is confined to the first twenty miles above the surface; most of the remaining atmosphere lies below the sixty-mile mark. It is often said, therefore, that space begins at an altitude of about 60 miles. Vehicles ascending above that point encounter little resistance to passage.

Research into the properties of the earth's atmosphere has accelerated since satellites became available in 1957 to make more extensive measurements. For information on reference tables, see *standard atmosphere.* For information on layers of the atmosphere, see *aerospace, exosphere, ionosphere, magnetosphere, mesosphere, stratosphere, thermosphere* and *troposphere.*

The atmospheres that envelop other heavenly bodies present hazards to astronauts of the future. Investigations will be necessary to determine whether an atmosphere is so thin that a spacecraft will have difficulty in braking to a soft landing (as on Mars) or whether elements of the atmosphere are toxic to human life.

attitude. Orientation or position of a spacecraft as determined by the inclination of the axes (roll, pitch, and yaw) to some frame of reference. In most cases, the frame of reference is fixed to the earth. However, Mariner 4, in its Mars fly-by in 1965, "locked on" to the star Canopus for an attitude reference. With one portion of the spacecraft always facing Canopus, and with another portion facing the sun, Mariner

4 remained fixed in position for its 228-day cruise from earth to the vicinity of Mars. See *Canopus*.

attitude control system. A combination of systems that function to keep a spacecraft properly oriented and counter any tendency to roll, pitch, or yaw. For instance, in Mariner 4's flight to the vicinity of Mars, the craft was kept in a stabilized attitude by gas jets, gyros, solar pressure vanes, jet vanes in the exhaust of the midcourse motor, solar and Canopus sensors, and associated electronics equipment. In manned flights, astronauts fire carefully calculated bursts from nozzles to change the attitude of a spacecraft.

Nimbus 2, which must always keep its cameras pointed directly at earth 700 miles below, uses two infrared horizon scanners to make certain that the spacecraft does not roll or swing away from the earth. The scanners seek out the earth's curvature, plus its heat, and feed the information into a 19-pound computer that serves as a pilot. For a small correction, the computer tells any of three flywheels—for roll, pitch, and yaw—to spin up and correct the satellite's attitude. For a major correction, the computer stops the flywheels and fires spurts of freon gas from nozzles.

Augmented Target Docking Adapter (ATDA). A stand-in for the Agena target vehicle in Project Gemini. After an Atlas-Agena nose-dived into the Atlantic in a 1966 launching, the ATDA became a substitute docking target for the Gemini 9 crew and averted the forty-five day delay that would have been required to obtain another Agena. McDonnell Aircraft developed the 1,700-pound ATDA (earth-orbit weight) by placing Gemini-spacecraft hardware inside a new shell and using a Lockheed-built target docking adapter—the device into which a Gemini spacecraft inserts its nose in a docking. The 11-foot-long barrel-shaped ATDA was given no rocket engine of its own and thus could not maneuver. As a consequence, it was nicknamed "the blob"—but its availability kept the Gemini series of missions moving.

aurora. Luminous streamers, arcs, or bands of light over great areas, usually in the arctic or antarctic regions. These displays are known as the Northern Lights (*aurora borealis*) or the Southern Lights (*aurora australis*). They are usually associated with solar flares and magnetic storms.

Aurora 7. The Mercury spacecraft that carried astronaut M. Scott Carpenter on the second American manned orbital flight. Aurora 7's flight was made on May 24, 1962, and, like John Glenn's journey, consisted of three orbits.

automatic countdown sequencer. Computer in a blockhouse that monitors events before a liftoff. It was an automatic countdown sequencer that stopped a Gemini 6 launch two seconds before scheduled liftoff on Dec. 12, 1965. The sequencer acted after a small electrical plug connecting the launch vehicle with the pad electrical system had dropped out prematurely. The plug dropout had started the flight programmer early, before sufficient time was allowed to build up full thrust for liftoff. The sequencer sensed the lack of thrust and sent a signal that shut down the engines.

automatic picture transmission (APT). Since Dec. 21, 1963, when TIROS 8 began orbiting with an automatic picture transmission camera, simple ground stations have been receiving daytime weather pictures sent directly from TIROS and Nimbus satellites. New capabilities were added in 1966 when Nimbus 2 began transmitting nighttime infrared photos by APT. APT sends weather photographs on the electronic slow-scan principle, similar to that used to transmit radio photographs. As a satellite orbits above a ground station, a "live" picture forms on the station's facsimile machine. A photo taken within range of a ground station can be processed and gridded on the ground within sixty seconds. See *Environmental Science Services Administration, Nimbus,* and *Television and Infrared Observation Satellite* (TIROS).

axis. Any of three fixed lines of reference in a space vehicle— longitudinal axis, normal axis, or lateral axis. The vehicle may make movements—yaw, pitch, or roll—around these axes. See *attitude.*

azimuth. Horizontal direction or bearing, measured in degrees from a fixed point, usually true north. The first Apollo/ Saturn 1B space vehicle, for example, was launched on an azimuth of 100° east of north.

Azusa. An Air Force tracking system that determines the distance, direction, and acceleration of a vehicle in flight. Instruments compare the shift in phase of a radio signal sent to the vehicle and returned from it.

B

backout. "An undoing of things already done in a countdown, usually in reverse order."—(NASA)

backup. An item or person kept in readiness to replace another, as a "backup pilot" designated to serve should the assigned pilot not be available for a mission.

Baikonour. See *Tyuratam.*

ballistic trajectory. The path followed by a vehicle after its engines cease to operate. The vehicle is acted upon only by gravity and aerodynamic drag. For instance, Mercury-Redstone 3, with Alan B. Shepard, Jr., aboard in 1961 made a ballistic flight—much like a projectile—from Cape Canaveral to a point 302 miles away in the Atlantic Ocean.

barber chair (colloquial). A spacecraft seat that can be adjusted to a reclining position so that the pilot achieves a greater tolerance to high acceleration.

BECO. See *booster engine cutoff.*

BEF. Verbal shorthand for "blunt end forward." Neil A. Armstrong, Gemini 8 command pilot, used the term in reviewing a situation; "We were in the 0–180–0 spacecraft configuration [flying backward], spacecraft BEF, hooked on to the Agena [docking target]."

bioastronautics. The field of study that considers the effect of space flight on life. For instance, scientists in this field choose the proper atmosphere for space cabins, help design improved space suits, and devise ways to cope with weightlessness and isolation.

biomedicine. "A combined discipline of biology and medicine directed toward analyzing human tolerance to environmental stress and providing protection in maintenance when such tolerances are exceeded."—(Air Force)

bionics. An interdisciplinary technical area concerned with creating nonliving systems that perform in a manner analogous to that of living systems. Bionics experts point out that a frog's eye may be studied as a model for a moving target indicator and that a bat's hearing system may provide clues for an airborne echo ranging device.

The Air Force has commented that research into bionic subsystems that simulate biological and neurophysiological principles "will lead to the development of machines capable of association, discrimination, and decision making for direct application in aerospace electronic systems." Air Force bionics studies are conducted at the Aeronautical Systems Division, Air Force Systems Command, Wright-Patterson Air Force Base, Ohio.

Biosatellite. The "Noah's Ark" or "Astrobug" spacecraft, used by NASA for the large-scale study of basic biology in space. A Biosatellite carries animals and plants in earth orbit for study of the effects of weightlessness, radiation, and the absence of the normal twenty-four-hour day-night cycle in space.

The Biosatellite program is designed to enable biologists to learn what happens to living organisms when gravity is reduced from $1g$ (as on earth) to virtually zero, or about $1/100,000$th of earth gravity (as in a satellite). Fears have been expressed that long space journeys by man may weaken muscles, cause the loss of calcium in bones, bring about deterioration of the circulatory system, and even curtail brain functioning. Satellite flights carrying monkeys, rodents, frog and sea urchin eggs, wheat seedlings, and other forms of life seek answers to these questions.

Successful completion of the program will show NASA "whether the effects of radiation on organisms in weightlessness are the same, greater, or less than they are known to be on the same organisms on earth."

On earth, the direction of root growth of a wheat seedling is determined by gravity; a Biosatellite experiment will determine the effect of zero gravity on this.

A Biosatellite is a seven-foot-long, 940-pound spacecraft consisting of three main sections—an adapter section which remains in orbit, a re-entry vehicle (a four-foot-long blunt

cone) which re-enters the earth's atmosphere over the
Pacific Ocean by deploying a parachute, and the experiment
capsule containing plants and animals. The Biosatellite is
built by General Electric Co., Reentry Systems Departments.
It is launched by a two-stage Thrust-Augmented Delta launch
vehicle. (All previous Deltas, before late 1966, used three
stages.)

Biosatellite 1 was launched successfully from Cape Kennedy on Dec. 14, 1966. However, the retrorockets failed to
fire on the fourth day, so that the capsule separated from the
adapter section and went into uncontrolled orbit, eventually
to drift into the atmosphere and burn up.

Biosatellite 2 made a 45-hour flight Sept. 7-9, 1967. Its
parachuted experiment capsule was caught at 12,000 feet by
an Air Force C-130 plane in the mid-Pacific.

Biosatellite flights were scheduled to continue through
1969, with the Office of Space Science and Applications and
the Ames Research Center in charge.

bioscience. NASA's bioscience programs include behavioral
biology, environmental biology, physical biology, exobiology,
biosatellites, and planetary quarantine. These programs are
conducted by NASA's Office of Space Science and Applications.

bird (colloquial). An inanimate object that flies, such as a
launch vehicle or a spacecraft.

bit (from *bi*nary digi*t*). A unit of information, as in "Mariner
4 is returning 33⅓ bits of information to earth per second."

black box (colloquial.) A single package that can be inserted
into a larger system. This term is usually applied to electronic
units.

Blackie and **Breezy.** Soviet space dogs which flew weightless
in orbit aboard Cosmos 110 in 1966. Blackie and Breezy
were held in place with slings and straps. Soviet scientists
reported later that upon landing the dogs showed marked
loss of calcium from bones and that muscles had shriveled.
Like human beings who have been bedridden, the dogs had
difficulty walking, but they recovered in a few days. The dogs
passed through radiation belts about 560 miles above the
earth, but reportedly showed no symptoms of cosmic radiation.

blackout. "1. A fadeout of radio communications due to ionospheric disturbances. 2. A fadeout of radio and telemetry transmission between ground stations and vehicles traveling at high speeds in the atmosphere caused by signal attenuation in passing through ionized boundary layer (plasma sheath) and shock wave regions generated by the vehicle."—(NASA)

During the "fireball" phase of their return from space and into the atmosphere, all U.S. manned spacecraft have suffered loss of telemetry and voice communications for about four minutes.

blastoff. A layman's term for a launching. In a countdown, the term is "liftoff."

blockhouse. A control center that houses electronic instruments used in launching a rocket. An advanced example is the steel and concrete blockhouse at NASA's Launch Complex 34, Cape Kennedy, standing about 1,000 feet from the pad from which Saturn 1 and 1B rockets have been fired. A 300-man blockhouse crew is protected against a rocket explosion by a dome-shaped roof designed to withstand a pressure of 2,188 pounds per square inch.

blockhouse measurements. Information sent from missile instruments to the launch control center during a countdown.

blowoff. An intentional explosion used to separate part of a vehicle from the rest during flight. The blast could, for instance, set free an instrument section for retrieval.

Blue Streak. A British space booster with two liquid-fueled Rolls Royce engines. It is the first stage of the Europa. Even though it veered off course, the Blue Streak flew a partly successful test at Woomera Range, Australia, in 1966. See *Europa.*

boilerplate. A metal copy of a flight model, such as Apollo Boilerplate 22, an engineering test version of the Apollo spacecraft. Boilerplate Apollos were used for tests of the Apollo spacecraft launch escape system at the White Sands Missile Range, N.M., in 1963, 1964, and 1965.

boiloff (colloquial). The vaporization of liquid oxygen, seen as a plume of white "smoke" when a liquid-fueled launch vehicle sits on a pad awaiting liftoff. The vaporization occurs when the temperature of the cold propellant rises because of its warmer surroundings and reaches its boiling point of minus 297° F.

bone demineralization. The loss of calcium from bones during prolonged weightless flight. For years doctors had recorded bone demineralization in patients confined to bed or in casts for long periods. The Gemini 7 crew, Frank Borman and James Lovell, proved that man could surmount this hazard in a fourteen-day flight. To determine the degree of calcium loss, a heel bone and a finger bone of each Project Gemini astronaut was X-rayed before and after each flight. The Space Medicine Division of NASA's Office of Manned Space Flight conducted the experiments.

booster. A short form for booster engine, which adds its thrust to that of a sustainer engine, or for a booster (first-stage) rocket. "Launch vehicle" is the preferred term for a complete rocket exclusive of its payload.

booster engine cutoff (BECO). Shutdown of the engines that lift a vehicle in its first portion of flight. On an Atlas launch vehicle, a BECO command shuts down the two outboard engines after a predetermined burn time, which is 2 minutes, 11.5 seconds after liftoff when it carries an Agena target vehicle. BECO is a part of the procedure known as "staging."

brain bank. A figurative name for a group of scientists from various disciplines who are placed in one laboratory or office to engage in systematic analysis. Experts from applied mathematics, economics, and other fields thus may exchange ideas, or "interact," to serve the purposes of industry and government. A brain bank is often given parklike surroundings to encourage its "far-out" research. Such a group also is sometimes called a "think tank."

braking. The slowing up of a space vehicle preparatory to landing on the moon or a planet. Braking presents obvious difficulties: spacecraft travel at tremendous speeds (Surveyor 1 was going 6,100 mph as it neared the moon), and the moon, Mars, and some other planets have atmospheres thinner than that of the earth.

One slowdown method is the parking orbit, or braking ellipse, in which the spacecraft circles the celestial body before beginning its descent. A second method, demonstrated by Surveyor 1, is that of firing a retrorocket, or braking rocket, opposite the direction of flight, after which small vernier engines are ignited and carefully throttled (with computer aid) to settle down slowly to the surface. A third method, proposed for landings on Mars and Venus, is the deployment of parachutes. See *planetary entry parachute*.

breakoff phenomenon. "The feeling which sometimes occurs during high-altitude flight of being totally separated and detached from the earth and human society. Also called the 'breakaway phenomenon.' "—(Air Force)

broadcast satellite. A proposed satellite that would be capable of broadcasting directly to conventional home frequency modulation (FM) radios, or to short-wave radios, or to both. In 1966 NASA authorized feasibility studies by the Missile and Space Division of General Electric Co. and the Astro-Electronics Division of the Radio Corporation of America.

Burner 2. A solid-fuel upper-stage vehicle. Burner 2 has full control and guidance capability, and can supply the final "kick" to put a small or medium payload either into earth orbit or into an earth-escape trajectory. It was designed for use as the second stage on the Thor booster, but it can also be used as an upper stage on other standard launch vehicles ranging in size up to Titan 3. The Boeing Space Division designed and built Burner 2 for the Air Force.

burn-in. See *debug*.

burnout. The point at which a rocket engine exhausts its fuel and ceases to operate.

C

CADFISS. See *Computation and Data Flow Integrated Subsystem.*

Canopus. The brightest star in the Southern Hemisphere, used by spacecraft as a fixed reference. Canopus is situated in the constellation Argo and is not visible in the northern and middle United States.

On a Surveyor journey to the moon, the spacecraft receives a command to fire its gas jets and roll slowly until a sensor "sees" the predicted brightness of Canopus. Then the sensor orders the roll to stop and "lock on" to the star to maintain the correct attitude for the rest of the journey. See *attitude.*

Cape Kennedy. Projecting from Florida's east coast, Cape Kennedy is the site of massive NASA, Air Force, and contractor installations for testing and launching spacecraft, launch vehicles, and missiles. Up to Nov. 28, 1963, the expanse of sand and scrub grass was known as Cape Canaveral. On that date, it was renamed by President Johnson for President Kennedy, who had been assassinated six days earlier. The site includes Station No. 1 of the Air Force Eastern Test Range. The NASA launch operations center known as the John F. Kennedy Space Center is situated on adjacent Merritt Island.

The site was approved by President Truman in 1949 for use as a space center. The Air Force has been launching spectacular shots there since 1950, when it fired a German V-2 rocket with an Army WAC Corporal second stage. Air Force activities at the site center at Patrick Air Force Base, which in the 1940's had been the Banana River Naval Air Station.

NASA, which had shared the facilities with the military for years, built its own facilities in the 1960's on land just north of the earlier launching pads. NASA's Launch Operations Center assembles and launches Saturn-Apollo vehicles and prepares for "follow-on" lunar and planetary missions. See *Air Force Eastern Test Range* and *Kennedy Space Center.*

capsule. As used in manned space flight: a passenger cabin that is sealed and pressurized so that a man can not only survive but also work effectively during launch, flight, and re-entry into the atmosphere.

captive firing. See *static firing.*

cavitation. The formation of vapor-filled cavities within a flowing liquid (such as a rocket propellant). Through vibration, this phenomenon can cause serious structural damage to rocket parts. Cavitation can be prevented by careful engineering design; equations of flow must be calculated to eliminate rapid velocity increases.

celestial mechanics. The study of the motions of bodies—either celestial bodies or space vehicles—in space. The study is chiefly concerned with application of the law of gravity.

Centaur. The world's first hydrogen-fueled space vehicle, Centaur is an upper stage developed for launching spacecraft to the moon and the planets. It is powered by two high-energy RL-10 engines that burn liquid hydrogen as a fuel and use a liquid oxygen oxidizer. Ignited in space, the engines develop a total of 30,000 pounds of thrust. NASA regards Centaur's performance as about 40 per cent better than that of vehicles using conventional kerosene-type fuels.

Designed to be flown atop an Atlas booster, Centaur can lift 8,500 tons of scientific equipment into earth orbit, 2,300 pounds to the moon, or 1,300 pounds to Mars or Venus. It is built by the Convair Division of General Dynamics and, like that firm's Atlas standard launch vehicle, keeps its shape through pressurization, eliminating the weight required for an internal framework.

Centaur's pioneering in liquid hydrogen technology dates from 1958, when the Advanced Research Projects Agency of the Defense Department set up a project to give the United States its first high-energy rocket vehicle. NASA's Marshall

Space Flight Center took over the program in 1960, and NASA's Lewis Research Center, in Cleveland, has managed the program since 1962. The Pratt and Whitney Aircraft Division of United Aircraft provides the engines. Honeywell supplies the inertial (self-contained) guidance system.

The upper stage made its first operational flight in 1966 as the Atlas-Centaur (AC-10) that launched a Surveyor spacecraft on a trajectory to intercept the moon for a soft landing.

Centaur ran up a string of seven straight successes in the Surveyor launches, and in early 1968 it took over from the older Atlas-Agena as the vehicle for unmanned high-altitude earth launches and interplanetary probes at Cape Kennedy.

Representative flight events as scheduled for the Centaur upper stage on a Surveyor launch to the moon are as follows:

Centaur Engine Start. Begins at 4 minutes, 11 seconds after liftoff, after the burned-out Atlas stage has been dropped. Starts at an altitude of 104 miles, downrange 234 miles from the launching pad, at a velocity of 7,600 mph.

Centaur Engine Cutoff. After a burn of 7 minutes, 14 seconds (at 11:25 into the flight), the two engines shut down. The Centaur has risen to 144 miles, traveled 1,740 miles downrange, and attained a velocity of 23,500 mph.

Spacecraft Separation. Occurs at 12 minutes, 37 seconds after liftoff. At 23,500 mph the Surveyor is injected into a path for direct ascent to the moon.

Centaur Reorientation. Begins at 12 minutes, 42 seconds after liftoff. Stage turns around (as in a half gainer).

Centaur Retrothrust. Begins at 16 minutes, 37 seconds after liftoff. The launch vehicle mission is completed at about 21 minutes after liftoff. The Centaur continues into space in a trajectory that bypasses the moon and stays clear of the spacecraft. (Altering the Centaur's trajectory eliminates the possibility that Surveyor's star-seeker will mistake Centaur for Canopus, on which it focuses for orientation.)

Salient facts about the Centaur upper stage:

Height: 30 ft. (48 ft. including the clamshell fairing that
   encloses Surveyor at liftoff)
Diameter: 10 ft.

Weight (before ignition): 37,500 lbs., less payload

Propellants: liquid hydrogen (fuel) and liquid oxygen (oxidizer)

Thrust (in space): 15,000 lbs. per engine

Tank: stainless steel 0.014 in. thick

centrifugal force. A force that pulls a revolving body outward.

centrifuge. A machine that simulates acceleration forces encountered in space flight by whirling animals or men at the end of a long boom. An outstanding centrifuge, or man-carrying motion generator, is that installed at NASA's Ames Research Center in 1967 to rotate a three-men cab. Driven by an 18,600-horsepower direct-current generator, it is rated as a "50*g*" centrifuge. See *G*.

centripetal force. A force that pulls a revolving body inward. An earth satellite is kept in orbit when its centrifugal and centripetal forces are equal.

chromosphere. The rosy-red layer of gases, or the "color ball," thousands of miles thick at the lower part of the sun's atmosphere.

circumlunar. A mission in which a spacecraft circles the moon.

cislunar space. Cislunar space lies between the earth and the moon. ("Cis" is Latin for "on this side.")

coasting flight. The flight of a launch vehicle between the engine cutoff of one stage and the engine start of the next stage, or between engine cutoff on the final stage and peak attitude.

cold welding. The phenomenon of surface adhesion or welding of two materials that come into contact under extremely high vacuum conditions—a problem that has resulted in costly failures of rockets and satellites. Cold welding has caused antennas to bind while unfurling and has caused fuel valves to jam. The Air Force is interested particularly in the effect of cold welding on switches employing frequent metal-to-metal surface contacts during space operations. To investigate the phenomenon, two nine-inch octahedral satellites were developed by TRW Systems under the direction of the Air Force Rocket Propulsion Laboratory at Edwards Air Force Base, Cal., and launched in 1966. The Air Force explained:

"Each satellite carries four solenoid valves and a solenoid

actuator, powered by batteries and solar cells located on the satellite's exterior. The valves and actuator have metal-to-metal mating surfaces that will be brought together thousands of times while the vehicles are in orbit. The mating surfaces, constructed of different combinations of materials, are constantly exposed to the space environment. Data collected will be used to assess the probability of cold welding occurring between typical space propulsion system materials."

command module. The control center that will house the three-man crew of an Apollo spacecraft. See *Apollo*.

Committee on Space Research (COSPAR). A committee within the International Council of Scientific Unions. COSPAR was created as an aftermath of the council's eighteen-month-long International Geophysical Year that ended Dec. 31, 1958. American, Soviet, and other scientists exchange information through papers presented at COSPAR meetings.

communications satellite. An earth-orbiting vehicle that relays signals between communications stations—say, from an English earth station to a U.S. earth station. In 1966 Early Bird, a communications satellite, enabled American television viewers to watch a championship boxing match "live" from London.

A communications satellite may be either active or passive. An active satellite acts essentially as a radio tower in space which receives, regenerates, and transmits signals; a passive satellite merely reflects signals. Because of its altitude, a communications satellite can relay signals that otherwise would be blocked by the earth's curvature. Microwaves, traveling in a straight line, are transmitted unaffected by lightning, solar radioactivity, or other atmospheric interferences.

The new communications era opened in 1958 when an Army Score satellite broadcast the first experimental voice message from space—a tape recording of President Eisenhower's Christmas message. In 1960 NASA launched the first passive satellite, Echo 1, an inflatable sphere off which signals were bounced. Then followed the active satellites Courier, Relay, Telstar, and Syncom (some in a series), and the passive Echo 2, so that by the time Early Bird was orbited in 1965 as the first commercial "bird," it was the thirteenth U.S. communications satellite.

Communications Satellite Corporation (Comsat). Comsat is the world's first commercial venture in space communications. It was incorporated in 1964 to set up a global communications network using commercial satellites.

Cosmat quickly sold its initial stock offering of 10 million shares—half to the public and half to communications companies, including 1.05 million to International Telephone and Telegraph and 2.9 million to American Telephone and Telegraph, its largest stockholder. The possibilities of this new form of global communications appealed so much to the

Early Bird, the world's first commercial communications satellite, built by the Communications Satellite Corporation, weighs approximately 85 pounds after it has been placed in a synchonous orbit above the earth.

"little" stockholder that great numbers rushed to get "in" at the beginning. In its first annual reports to its stockholders, Comsat commented, "More than half of the public shareholders own 10 or fewer shares each."

The corporation launched its first satellite, Early Bird, on Apr. 6, 1965, using a Thrust-Augmented Delta rocket and NASA facilities, for which it paid NASA. Early Bird went into a synchronous orbit over the equator at longitude 27.5° W at an altitude of almost 22,300 miles. This position enabled Early Bird to look down on the eastern United States, South America, western Europe, and Africa. Commercial service began June 28 with a telephone call from President Johnson to Britain's Prime Minister Harold Wilson, West Germany's Chancellor Ludwig Erhard, and others.

Comsat's capabilities in communications increased swiftly. Early Bird, an 85-pound cylinder built by Hughes Aviation Co., had a capacity of 240 two-way channels in which it handled telephone and telegraph traffic, data and facsimile transmissions, and intercontinental television. Comsat soon had made plans for two successively larger satellites—a 160-pound improved version, also by Hughes, for 1966, and for 1968 a 240-pound model with a capacity of 1,200 two-way circuits. TRW, Inc., received the last-named contract. Comsat officials also began talks leading toward creation of a satellite system to serve domestic TV networks and to handle other services such as telephone, telegraph, and data transmission.

In the global network, Comsat signed agreements with foreign telecommunications entities for joint ownership of the "space segment" of a satellite system. At least twenty-five countries were expected to have ground stations by the 1970's. (Comsat's U.S. ground stations are located at Andover, Me.; Brewster Flat, Wash.; and Paumalu, Oahu, Hawaii.) The new technology of satellite communications is expected to lead to new methods and a far greater volume of international communications.

communications satellite ships. Vessels that communicate with satellites 22,300 miles above the earth (in the "synchronous corridor") and play a particularly important part in space missions.

It was a communications satellite ship, the Navy's *Kings-*

port, which relayed to NASA the voice contact from Gemini 8 over the western Pacific reporting that it had undocked from the Agena after the historic link-up of the two spacecraft in 1966. The sequence of events: from 185 miles high and not far from the Philippines, Gemini 8 beamed voice and spacecraft telemetry to an instrumentation ship, the Navy's *Coastal Sentry.* The *Coastal Sentry* sent the transmission to the nearby *Kingsport.* In turn, the *Kingsport* beamed the signal to Syncom 3, a synchronous satellite. Syncom 3 instantly relayed the transmission to a land station in Hawaii. Cable and landline circuits carried the message to the NASA Communications Network (NASCOM) in Greenbelt, Md., and on to NASA's Mission Control Center at Houston, Texas.

The *Kingsport,* a 455-foot former Victory Ship, carries on her afterdeck a 30-foot parabolic "dish" antenna within a 54-foot radome. In 1963, while anchored in the harbor at Lagos, Nigeria, the *Kingsport* first demonstrated ship-to-satellite communications by sending a message to Syncom 2, hovering overhead in the South Atlantic, and back, for a round trip of about 45,000 miles.

Computation and Data Flow Integrated Subsystem (CADFISS). In this procedure a NASA computer at Goddard Space Flight Center, Greenbelt, Md., makes a system-by-system, station-by-station, computer-programmed checkout of the worldwide communications network supporting manned space flights. CADFISS certifies the network's readiness before flights. During flights, CADFISS checks on the readiness of those stations that are temporarily beyond electronic range—that is, acquisition range—of the orbiting spacecraft.

computer. On the ground and in space, the computer has become an indispensable part of the U.S. space program, instantly performing complex mathematical tasks that man alone could not accomplish soon enough to be of any value on a space flight.

From launch through impact, the Real-Time Computer Complex at the NASA Manned Spacecraft Center, Houston, supports each manned mission by handling data for information and control. Other computers check countdown details automatically and shut down rocket engines when necessary to avoid catastrophe, steer launch vehicles, or handle other assignments. But the most dramatic single display of capabilities came when a 59-pound on-board guidance computer —no bigger than a hatbox—enabled Gemini 6 to calculate velocity and altitude changes and achieve history's first rendezvous in space (with Gemini 7). See *analog computer, digital computer,* and *Real-Time Computer Complex.*

Comsat. See *Communications Satellite Corporation.*

configuration. The contour, or size and shape, produced by the relative disposition and make-up of component parts. Thus the configuration of a Saturn 5 launch vehicle is described as a five-engine first stage, a five-engine second stage, and a single-engine third stage.

corona. The layer of gases, or the "crown," outside the sun. The corona is only faintly luminous, and ordinarily is seen only during a total eclipse of the sun.

cosmic dust. Meteoroids so small that they appear to be dust particles.

cosmic noise. Natural radio signals originating in outer space.

cosmic rays. High-energy charged nuclear particles moving through space. They are believed to originate from (1) small disturbed areas on the sun and (2) from interstellar sources far beyond our solar system. Most of the particles are hydrogen nuclei. However, some are nuclei of helium and the heavier elements.

The galactic cosmic ray particles originating from interstellar space have far higher energies than solar cosmic rays. NASA's interplanetary spacecraft carry experiments to measure the characteristics of both solar and galactic cosmic rays.

cosmonaut. The USSR's name for its space travelers, or astronauts. See *astronaut.*

Cosmos. A series of USSR satellites, of which more than 200 have been launched. The Soviet's announce all as scientific satellites and have given scientific results of some flights, but U.S. officials have long considered part of them as reconnaissance or "spy" satellites. No dimensions have been announced. Most Cosmos satellites have been put into relatively low orbits, typically about 125 by 200 miles, but others fly in orbits about 800 by 1,050 miles. Some have had rather short lifetimes. In a number of launches, the Soviets have used a single vehicle to place five Cosmos satellites in orbit at once.

Pairs of Cosmos satellites in low orbit have been used successfully to demonstrate automatic docking.

COSPAR. See *Committee on Space Research*.

countdown. The sequence of events leading to the launching of a space vehicle. A countdown follows a timetable step by step, but it may be interrupted by a "hold" to permit further checking and preparation. The count leads downward to T (for Time). There it reaches the objective—liftoff.

The typical countdown that follows was used at Cape Kennedy when a two-stage Titan 2 Gemini launch vehicle boosted Neil A. Armstrong and David R. Scott into orbit in Gemini 8:

T minus 720 minutes: Begin propellant loading.

T minus 420 minutes: Backup flight crew reports to the 100-foot level of the White Room to participate in final flight preparations.

T minus 390 minutes: Complete propellant loading.

T minus 300 minutes: Begin terminal countdown.

T minus 270 minutes: Primary crew awakened.

T minus 240 minutes: Medical examination.

T minus 220 minutes: Breakfast.

T minus 195 minutes: Crew leaves quarters.

T minus 185 minutes: Crew arrives at ready room on Pad 16.

T minus 135 minutes: Purging of suit begins.

T minus 124 minutes: Crew leaves ready room.

T minus 120 minutes: Crew to Complex 19.

T minus 119 minutes: Crew arrives at 100-foot level.

T minus 115 minutes: Crew enters spacecraft.

T minus 100 minutes: Close spacecraft hatches.

T minus 70 minutes: White Room evacuation.

T minus 55 minutes: Begin erector lowering.

T minus 20 minutes: Static firing of spacecraft orbital attitude maneuvering system (OAMS).

T minus 3 minutes: Built-in hold.

T minus 3 seconds: Launch vehicle ignition.

T minus 0 seconds: Liftoff.

T plus 2 minutes, 36 seconds: Booster engine cutoff (BECO).

T plus 5 minutes, 41 seconds: Second stage engine cutoff (SECO). This occurs about 530 miles from Cape Kennedy at a velocity of about 17,400 mph.

T plus 5 minutes, 57 seconds: Engine tailoff has increased the velocity to about 17,500 mph, and the crew separates the Gemini spacecraft from the Titan 2 launch vehicle by firing the OAMS thrusters. This adds 10 feet per second to the velocity.

T plus 6 minutes, 7 seconds: The spacecraft is inserted into an elliptical orbit 100 by 139 miles high.

countup. The term sometimes used for the sequence of events after liftoff; the "T plus" developments.

Courier. A U.S. Army experimental communications satellite that in 1960 demonstrated its ability to receive, store, and transmit signals sent to it from ground stations. Courier circled the earth from 501 to 658 miles high and functioned successfully for twenty days.

crawler. A transporter used to carry the mammoth Saturn 5 rocket and its service tower 3.5 miles from NASA's Vehicle Assembly Building to a launch pad. The crawler itself qualifies as one of the sights at the Merritt Island Launch Area's Complex 39, for it weighs 6 million pounds and has a platform 131 feet long by 114 feet wide—bigger than a baseball infield. Height may be adjusted from 20 to 26 feet. The crawler moves on four double-tracked treads—a clue to its ancestry, for it is a modified version of giant coal-stripping shovels built by the same builder, the Marion Power Shovel Company. The combined weight of the crawler and its load —the mobile launcher plus the Saturn 5–Apollo space vehicle—runs about 12 million pounds. Maximum speed when loaded: one mile per hour.

creep. The permanent distortion or deforming of a metal from stress. High temperatures accelerate creep.

cryogenic propellants. Rocket propellants that remain liquid only at very low temperatures. They include liquid hydrogen, a fuel which must be produced and stored below its boiling point of minus 422° F. Liquid oxygen, an oxidizer, is also cryogenic, as its boiling point stands at minus 297° F. The branch of physics that deals with the production and effects of very low temperatures is called cryogenics.

cutoff. In rocketry: the act of shutting off an engine or engines.

D

data acquisition facility. See *acquisition.*

debug. "1. To isolate and remove malfunctions from a device. 2. Specifically, in electronic manufacturing, to operate equipment under specified environmental and test conditions in order to eliminate early failures and to stabilize equipment prior to actual use. Also called burn-in."—(NASA)

Deep Space Network (DSN). A NASA network for tracking and two-way communications with unmanned vehicles in deep space. DSN is separate from the Manned Spaced Flight Tracking Network, which tracks Gemini and Apollo spacecraft, and from the Scientific Satellite Network, which tracks earth-orbiting weather, communications, and scientific satellites.

DSN stations are situated at Goldstone (Cal.) Space Communications Station, the primary station of the network, and at Johannesburg, South Africa; Woomera and Canberra, Australia; and Madrid, Spain. Goldstone has a 210-foot tracking and telemetry antenna as well as 85-foot antennas; all other U.S. stations have 85-foot antennas. A monitoring station at Cape Kennedy also supports the network.

The Jet Propulsion Laboratory of the California Institute of Technology provides system management and technical direction for the network. The overseas stations are operated and staffed by their own governments, with the assistance of U.S. personnel. See *antennas* and *Goldstone "210."*

Delta (and Thrust-Augmented Delta, known as TAD). A family of three-stage launch vehicles, reliable NASA workhorses that have successfully placed research, weather, and communications satellites into earth orbit. The McDonnell Douglas Corp. produces the Delta for NASA.

450 LB PAYLOAD
IN 500 N. MI.
CIRCULAR ORBIT

1,100 LB PAYLOAD
IN 500 N. MI.
CIRCULAR ORBIT

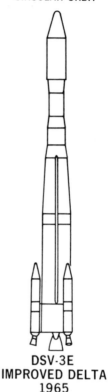

DM 19

1960

DSV-3E
IMPROVED DELTA
1965

Delta was created in 1960 by joining an Air Force intermediate-range Thor missile with a pair of upper-stage rockets.
At that time it could carry up to 500 pounds into a 300-
nautical-mile circular orbit. In 1962, as space assignments
grew increasingly difficult, Douglas adopted a more powerful
Thor first-stage (booster) rocket having a thrust of 172,000
pounds. The second-stage propellant tank was stretched three
feet later in 1962 to increase burning time, and a more
powerful third stage was developed in 1963. The Thrust-
Augmented Delta made its debut in 1964, taking its name
from the strapping on of three solid-propellant rocket motors

at equal distances around the base of the Thor first stage. The solid rockets augment first-stage thrust by 160,000 pounds for the first thirty-four seconds of flight, enabling TAD to hurl up to 1,200 pounds into a 300-nautical-mile circular orbit. Thus Delta's useful payload more than doubled between 1960 and 1964. In 1965, Delta was improved further with the substitution of a bigger second stage; the new version, the DSV-3E, had a lifting capacity of 1,300 pounds of payload.

Delta launch vehicles have had a particularly close relationship with the nation's program of experimental communications satellites. They have put into orbit Echo 1, Relay 1 and 2, Syncom 1, 2, and 3; Telstar 1 and 2, and Early Bird. They have also lofted the famous TIROS and ESSA weather satellites. Over the years Delta payloads have varied in weight from the 80-pound Explorer 10 to the 545-pound Orbiting Solar Observatory 2, and in diameter from the 28-inch-diameter Syncom 1 to the 100-foot Echo 1.

Delta stands 94.5 feet tall and measures 8 feet in diameter. It weighs 150,000 pounds, including the solids. Its first two stages have liquid-propellant engines. The third stage and the strap-ons are solid rockets. Bell Telephone Laboratories provides guidance equipment.

Data on the Delta stages:

First stage: Modified Douglas Thor missile with North American Rocketdyne engine burning RP-1 or kerosene and liquid oxygen. *Thrust:* 172,000 lbs. *Burning time:* 2 min., 20 sec.

First stage strap-on (for TAD only): Three Thiokol solid rockets. *Thrust:* 160,000 lbs. *Action time:* 34 sec.

Second stage: Aerojet-General engine burning inhibited red fuming nitric acid and unsymmetrical dimethylhydrazine. *Thrust:* about 7,600 lbs. *Burning time:* 6 min., 25 sec.

Third stage: Motors available are:

1. Hercules. *Thrust* (average): 6,193 lbs. *Action time:* 22.5 sec.

2. United Technology Center. *Thrust* (average): 5,624 lbs. *Action time:* 30.5 sec.

3. Thiokol. *Thrust* (average): 9,983 lbs. *Action time:* 41.6 sec.

Of the first 54 satellites launched by Delta, 51 went into orbit. The record of successful Delta launches:

Delta Number	Mission	Date
2	Echo 1	Aug. 12, 1960
3	TIROS 2	Nov. 23, 1960
4	Explorer 10	Mar. 25, 1961
5	TIROS 3	July 12, 1961
6	Explorer 12	Aug. 16, 1961
7	TIROS 4	Feb. 8, 1962
8	OSO 1	Mar. 7, 1962
9	Ariel 1 (British)	Apr. 26, 1962
10	TIROS 5	June 19, 1962
11	Telstar 1	July 10, 1962
12	TIROS 6	Sept. 18, 1962
13	Explorer 14	Oct. 2, 1962
14	Explorer 15	Oct. 27, 1962
15	Relay 1	Dec. 13, 1962
16	Syncom 1	Feb. 14, 1963
17	Explorer 17	Apr. 2, 1963
18	Telstar 2	May 7, 1963
19	TIROS 7	June 19, 1963
20	Syncom 2	July 26, 1963
21	Explorer 18 (IMP 1)	Nov. 26, 1963
22	TIROS 8	Dec. 21, 1963
23	Relay 2	Jan. 21, 1964
25	Syncom 3	Aug. 19, 1964
26	Explorer 21 (IMP 2)	Oct. 3, 1964
27	Explorer 26	Dec. 21, 1964
28	TIROS 9	Jan. 22, 1965
29	OSO 2	Feb. 3, 1965
30	Early Bird	Apr. 6, 1965
31	Explorer 28 (IMP 3)	May 29, 1965
32	TIROS 10	July 1, 1965
34	GEOS 1 (Explorer 29)	Nov. 6, 1965
35	Pioneer 6	Dec. 16, 1965
36	ESSA 1	Feb. 3, 1966
37	ESSA 2	Feb. 28, 1966
38	Explorer 32	May 25, 1966
39	Explorer 33	July 1, 1966
40	Pioneer 7	Aug. 17, 1966

41	ESSA 3 (TOS-A)	Oct. 2, 1966
42	Intelsat 2A	Oct. 26, 1966
43	Biosatellite 1	Dec. 14, 1966
44	Intelsat 2B	Jan. 11, 1967
45	ESSA 4	Jan. 26, 1967
46	OSO 3	Mar. 8, 1967
47	Intelsat 2 (F-3)	Mar. 22, 1967
48	Explorer 34	May 24, 1967
49	Explorer 35	July 19, 1967
50	Intelsat 2D	Sept. 27, 1967
51	OSO 4	Oct. 18, 1967
52	ESSA 6 and Pioneer 8	Nov. 10, 1967
53	TTS 1	Dec. 13, 1967
54	GEOS 2	Jan. 11, 1968

demineralization. See *bone demineralization.*

design studies. "Studies conducted to determine the characteristics of a system needed to satisfy a particular requirement." —(Air Force)

destruct system. Equipment within a rocket to destroy it deliberately if the rocket goes off course after being launched but before reaching orbit.

Diamant. A three-stage French space rocket rated at 62,000 pounds of thrust. It boosted the first French satellite, the A-1, into orbit in 1965 from Hammaguir in the Algerian Sahara.

Diapason. France's second satellite, launched from Hammaguir, Algeria, on Feb. 17, 1966. It was a test satellite and was used for geodetic measurements.

digital computer. A computing machine that works on the principle of counting, in contrast to an analog computer, which measures. Its stored programs of instructions guide launch vehicles and set patterns for other precise maneuvers in space flight.

direct ascent. A flight to the moon or planets without going into a parking orbit around earth. Surveyor 1 was launched by an Atlas-Centaur vehicle into a direct-ascent lunar trajectory. (With a single burn, Centaur accelerated Surveyor 1 to escape velocity. In an alternate procedure, an upper-stage vehicle puts a spacecraft into parking orbit, shuts down, and at the proper moment re-ignites to launch the spacecraft into a lunar trajectory.)

Discoverer. A series of Air Force satellites. They contributed pioneering information in 1960 on recovery of capsules from water and in mid-air. Later Discoverers explored effects of exposure to space environment. But for years no Discoverer payloads have been revealed in this military space program.

Discoverer 1, launched Feb. 28, 1959, by a Thor-Hustler rocket on the Western Test Range, was the first U.S. satellite to go into a polar orbit (over the South and North Poles rather than circling the equator).

On Aug. 11, 1960, Discoverer 13, in polar orbit, dropped an instrument capsule into the Pacific so that Navy frogmen and helicopters could carry out the first recovery from water —a prelude to Mercury and Gemini recoveries. Eight days later, Discoverer 14 dropped a capsule that a C-119 Flying Boxcar caught in a dangling trapeze-like snare at an altitude of 8,500 feet.

docking. The interlocking of vehicles in space. Docking was first accomplished on Mar. 16, 1966, when astronauts Neil Armstrong and David Scott linked their Gemini 8 spacecraft with an unmanned Agena spacecraft, or target vehicle. See *Gemini*. The Russians have experimented with automatic docking, and completed successful tests of this method using pairs of unmanned Cosmos satellites on Oct. 30, 1967, and Apr. 15, 1968.

Doppler shift. The change of frequency in vibrations, as in the whistle of a train approaching, passing, and going away from the listener. The Doppler shift is employed in tracking and navigation systems. Changes are interpreted to determine velocity and location. It is based on the change in frequency with which energy reaches a receiver when the source of radiation or a reflector of the radiation and the receiver are in motion relative to each other.

drogue. A small conical parachute used to stabilize a spacecraft as it nears a landing. The Apollo spacecraft carries in its earth landing system two nylon conical ribbon drogue parachutes thirteen feet in diameter. The drogues are deployed first, at about 25,000 feet, to stabilize the Apollo blunt end forward, before the pilot and main chutes are deployed. See *earth landing system*.

droppables. Items that may be dropped during the ascent of a launch vehicle. Lockheed's Agena upper stage, for instance, may be lightened by 509 pounds by releasing the following items as it climbs: adapter and attachments to a Thor first stage, 280 pounds; start charge, 1 pound; destruct system, 11 pounds; retrorockets, 10 pounds; horizon sensor fairings, 7 pounds, and nose shroud, 200 pounds.

DSN. See *Deep Space Network*.

Dyna-Soar (X-20). An experimental piloted, winged space glider once under development by the Air Force. Dyna-Soar died in 1963 when the program was canceled, but some of its projects (full pressure suit, heat protection system, and others) lived on when the Air Force was assigned responsibility for developing a near-earth Manned Orbiting Laboratory. Dyna-Soar was to have been rocketed into orbital flight by a Titan 3 launch vehicle and a pilot was to fly the craft back through the earth's atmosphere and set it down on land completely under his own control.

Early Bird. See *Communications Satellite Corporation.*

Earth. The third planet from the sun (at 93 million miles). Traveling at a speed of 18.52 miles per second, the earth revolves about the sun once every 365.25 days. Its nearest planetary neighbors are Venus, which is closer to the sun (at 67 million miles), and Mars, which is farther from the sun (at 142 million miles).

Slightly pear-shaped, as the satellite Vanguard 1 discovered in 1958, the earth measures 7,927 miles in diameter at the equator. It is fifth in size among the planets—far smaller than Jupiter, Saturn, Uranus, and Neptune.

That most of the earth's surface—71 per cent—is water helped the United States in its recovery of manned spacecraft in earth-orbital flights in the 1960's. The earth's rotation about its axis once every twenty-four hours also affected the flight path of earth-orbiting manned spacecraft: as a Gemini craft orbited, the earth turned beneath it, so that on each ascending pass across the equator, the craft regressed about 22.5°.

What makes the earth different from all other planets in the solar system, so far as is known, is that its atmosphere is the only one capable of sustaining human life. Ninety-nine per cent of this atmosphere lies below the twenty-mile mark. Almost all of the other one per cent lies below the 60-mile mark.

earth landing system. On the Apollo spacecraft, this system consists of a sequence controller and three kinds of parachutes: (1) two nylon conical ribbon drogues 13 feet in diameter; (2) three nylon main pilot chutes, 7 feet in diameter; (3) three nylon main chutes 83.5 feet in diameter. The sequencer opens and closes switches to initiate steps in the landing. After the apex heat shield has been blown away by pyrotechnics at 25,000 feet, the drogue chutes are shot out by mortar to stabilize the Apollo blunt end forward. At 12,000 feet the pilot chutes billow out, and they pull the main chutes from their containers.

Earth Resources Observation Satellite (EROS). A satellite, not yet developed, that the U.S. Department of the Interior hopes to have in operation in 1969. EROS would make use of advanced sensors to chart pollution patterns, measure the shift of glaciers, record the growth of river deltas, and observe natural resources in other ways.

Eastern Test Range. See *Air Force Eastern Test Range.*

eccentric orbit. An orbit deviating from the line of a circle, thus forming an ellipse. The eccentricity of the earth's orbit is 0.016751. (A circle equals 0). It is just about impossible to launch an earth satellite into a completely circular orbit, but precise firing of its own propulsion system can maneuver it into a circular orbit. Thus Gemini was launched into a 100-by-169-mile orbit; then, using sixteen thrusters, it propelled itself into a 185-mile circular orbit. Some orbits of unmanned scientific spacecraft are purposely made highly eccentric—that is, very lopsided—so that they can pass through specific distant areas. For instance, Orbiting Geophysical Observatory 1 was put into an orbit of 175 by 92,-721 miles.

Echo. A series of passive communications satellites. Echo 1, an inflated sphere 100 feet in diameter, became the world's first such satellite on Aug. 12, 1960. Among other experiments, it reflected radio voice signals from the Bell Telephone Laboratories in New Jersey to the Jet Propulsion Laboratory in California, and thus proved that communications could be sent from point to point on earth by bouncing signals off a satellite.

Launched by a Thor-Delta, the 132-pound Echo 1 was carried folded in a 28-inch spherical container until it reached orbital velocity. Then the container was discarded and the balloon inflated. Its surface—Du Pont Mylar polyester film covered with vapor-deposited aluminum—gave Echo 1 the intensity of a bright star, making it readily visible to ground watchers. Echo 1's skin measured only 0.00050 inch thick. Solar pressure affected the balloon satellite, so that its perigee, initially 945 miles, dropped to 781 miles within ten weeks. Although its gas supply has leaked out through holes made by micrometeoroids, Echo 1 remains in orbit.

Echo 2, orbited on Jan. 25, 1964, was somewhat larger— 135 feet in diameter—and about twenty times more rigid than its predecessor. Echo 2's skin was a laminate of aluminum foil and polymer plastic 0.00075 inch thick. Neither Echo satellite carried a receiver or transmitter.

ecliptic. "Plane of the earth's orbit around the sun. It is used as a reference for other interplanetary orbits. Also the name for the apparent path of the sun through the constellations as projected on the celestial sphere."—(Air Force)

The orbit of the nearest planet, Mars, has an inclination (tilt) of only 1.5° to the ecliptic. The orbit of Venus has an inclination of 3.2°. Thus both lie nearly in the same plane as the earth.

ELDO. See *European Launcher Development Organization.*
electric rocket engine. See *ion propulsion.*
Electron. A USSR satellite employed, the news agency Tass said, to study the earth's internal and external radiation belts and physical phenomena connected with them. In 1964, two pairs were launched. Each launching was carried out by a single vehicle. Each Electron flies an exceedingly lopsided orbit, as typified by Electron 4, with an apogee of 41,158 miles and a perigee of only 285 miles.

engine. In a liquid-propellant rocket, the machine that transforms energy into work. (But a solid-propellant rocket is said to have a motor.) For facts on powerful engines used in Saturn launch vehicles, see *F-1, H-1,* and *J-2.*

Enos. A 37.5-pound, five-and-a-half-year-old chimpanzee who orbited the earth twice in a Mercury spacecraft on Nov. 29, 1961. Enos demonstrated his ability to perform psychomotor tests while his capsule flew through space, and he was recovered safe and well from the Atlantic Ocean 260 miles south of Bermuda. The astro-chimp's flight preceded that of John Glenn, who within three months became the first American to orbit the earth. In addressing a joint meeting of the U.S. Senate and House of Representatives, Glenn drew a laugh when he commented on his introduction to President Kennedy's five-year-old daughter, Caroline, just after his historic flight. Glenn told Congress: "I think that Caroline really cut us down to size and put us in proper position when, after being introduced, she looked and said, 'Where's the monkey?' "

Environmental Research Satellite (ERS). A satellite that weighs only from 1.5 to 9 pounds and travels as a "hitchhiker" on a launch vehicle engaged in a major mission. An ERS often acts as a "test bed" to carry unproved components into space before their use in later generations of spacecraft. The builder, TRW Systems, installs solar cells on all exterior surfaces of an ERS, enabling it to convert the sun's energy into electricity. Thus no battery is required. The many-sided satellites are so designed that at any time about 15 per cent of the cells are exposed to the sun.

Environmental Science Services Administration (ESSA). This agency is part of the U.S. Department of Commerce. In a joint effort with NASA, it conducts a national operational weather satellite program. Its satellites include ESSA 1 and ESSA 2—285-pound spin-stabilized TIROS cylindrical models that roll in earth orbits like a wheel, taking pictures of the cloud cover with cameras placed on opposite sides of the wheel. See *automatic picture transmission*.

One ESSA was launched in 1966 and three more in 1967, all from the Western Test Range in California and all successfully. The Radio Corporation of America is the prime contractor for this satellite.

Eole (French for Aeolus, god of the winds in Greek mythology). A joint French-American balloon-and-satellite project to develop a new way to gather weather data for long-range forecasting. France's National Center for Space Studies and NASA agreed in 1966 to set up a network of instrumented constant-level balloons to drift with the wind at high altitudes and act as tracers of air masses. A satellite was to circle the earth and "interrogate" each balloon periodically. In passing nearby, the satellite would record data on pressure, temperature, and location telemetered from the balloon for later transmission to ground stations.

equatorial orbit. An earth orbit whose plane is in or near the earth's equatorial plane.

EROS. See *Earth Resources Observation Satellite.*

ERS. See *Environmental Research Satellite.*

ESRO. See *European Space Research Organization.*

escape velocity. The speed that a space vehicle must attain to overcome the pull of the earth's gravity and travel outward into space. The escape velocity at or near the earth's surface is more than seven miles per second, or about 25,000 mph. A single-stage vehicle with enough initial thrust to accelerate to 25,000 mph could break away from the earth's gravity and escape into space. However, the usual method is to use the first rocket stage to lift the vehicle up through the dense atmosphere, and then to fire one or more additional stages to attain the desired velocity. Because the earth's gravity declines at higher altitudes, the escape velocity also falls, and at an altitude of 500 miles it is 23,600 mph.

For the moon and the inner planets, the escape velocities are relatively small: 1.5 miles per second for the moon; 3.2, for Mercury; 6.3, for Venus; and 3.1, for Mars. However, the escape velocities are much higher for the outer planets (except tiny Pluto): 37.3 miles per second for Jupiter; 22.4, for Saturn; 13.1, for Uranus; and 14.3, for Neptune.

ESSA. See *Environmental Science Services Administration.*

Europa. A three-stage launch vehicle that will consist of Britain's Blue Streak as the first stage, the French Coralie as the second stage, and a West German third stage. In 1965 the Blue Streak made three flights, and in 1966 it lifted dummy second and third stages at Australia's Woomera range. The European Launcher Development Organization is handling the venture.

Europa 1, launched in a two-stage version at Woomera on Aug. 4, 1967, failed when the second stage did not ignite.

European Launcher Development Organization (ELDO). A multi-nation organization formed to develop a launch vehicle. Through sharing of costs, with Britain, France, and West Germany assigned the major portions, the free industrialized nations of Europe hoped to close the technology gap between them and the space leaders, the United States and the USSR. Each of the three principal nations was assigned a rocket stage to develop, and Australia provided the Woomera range for the first suborbital launching of the vehicle, the Europa, in

1966. Belgium and the Netherlands also are members of ELDO.

European Space Research Organization (ESRO). An organization with ten member countries—Belgium, Britain, Denmark, France, Italy, the Netherlands, Spain, Sweden, Switzerland, and West Germany. Its satellites are designed to carry scientific experiments to study cosmic and solar radiation.

ESRO 2, its first satellite, failed to go into polar orbit when launched from the Western Test Range, Cal., on May 29, 1967. ESRO 2 was launched by NASA on a Scout rocket, which apparently had a malfunction in its third-stage burn so that the fourth stage did not ignite. The prime contractor for the 163-pound satellite was Hawker Siddeley Dynamic, Ltd., of Britain.

ESRO 1 was to be launched later, out of sequence.

In 1967 the European organization signed an agreement to have its 230-pound Highly Elliptical Orbiting Satellite (HEOS) launched by NASA aboard a Delta rocket in 1968. HEOS was designed to range far from earth to study the interplanetary magnetic field and solar and cosmic ray particles.

EVA. See *extravehicular activity*.

exobiology. The study of living organisms on other planets. The Space Science Board of the National Academy of Sciences has advocated a strong program of unmanned planetary spacecraft to carry forward the work of exobiology.

exosphere. "The region of the atmosphere above the thermosphere, beginning at roughly 600 kilometers [about 373 miles] where the density is so low that an upward-traveling molecule makes no further collisions until it falls back to the base of the exosphere, or exceeding escape velocity, it escapes from the atmosphere entirely. At an altitude of roughly 10,000 kilometers [about 6,200 miles], the density of the exosphere merges into the density of the interplanetary medium. The exosphere overlaps the magnetosphere."—(American Institute of Physics)

Explorer. A series of geophysical satellites and probes, varying greatly in shapes and sizes. Explorers investigate the upper atmosphere and space near earth. More than thirty Explorers have supplied valuable information on micrometeoroids, radiation, magnetic field, solar plasma, and temperatures and pressures.

Explorer 1. On Jan. 31, 1958, after the USSR had launched Sputniks 1 and 2, Explorer 1 became the first American earth satellite. Explorer 1 made the most important discovery of the International Geophysical Year by confirming the existence of a radiation belt around the earth (Pioneer 3 later found a second belt). A State University of Iowa physicist, Dr. James A. Van Allen, set up a Geiger-Mueller counter for a cosmic radiation measuring experiment on board, and the radiation belts were given his name. The satellite was boosted into orbit with a Jupiter C vehicle (a Redstone rocket plus three solid stages) by an Army Ballistic Missile Agency–Jet Propulsion Laboratory team. At an inclination of 33° to the equator, it began flight with an apogee of 1,573 miles and a perigee of 224 miles.

Interplanetary Explorer. The designation of a series of spacecraft that continues to bear Explorer numbers (from Explorer 18 in 1963). These craft gather data on space phenomena between the earth and the moon.

The first IMP, the 138-pound Explorer 18, launched Nov. 27, 1963, flew out farther from earth—122,800 miles —than any other earth satellite up to that time. Its data showed that the earth's magnetic field is shaped like a teardrop. Explorer 18 has a highly lopsided orbit, approaching to within 119 miles of the earth, and it is expected to remain in orbit for hundreds of years.

Through 1967 NASA had launched six IMP's, of which two were designed to collect information at lunar distances. The sixth IMP—the 230-pound Explorer 35—launched July 19, 1967, was placed into a highly elliptical earth orbit that carried it beyond the distance of the moon and back. Thus Explorer 35 was "anchored" in interplanetary space and traveled much of the time away from the influence of the earth's magnetic field.

extravehicular activity (EVA). An activity by an astronaut outside his spacecraft, such as a "space walk." There are two kinds: (1) The umbilical EVA, in which an astronaut attached to a spacecraft by a heavy cord moves about with the aid of a maneuvering unit. (2) A standup EVA, in which the astronaut lifts the hatch cover of the spacecraft and stands in his seat with the upper half of his body in space for tasks such as picture taking.

The maneuvering unit may be either an HHMU (hand-held maneuvering unit or "space gun") or an AMU (astronaut maneuvering unit or "backpack").

EVA conducted during the Gemini flights revealed that work in space is more tiring than had been expected. Astronauts tended to drift away from their work sites. However, new techniques were developed for the final Gemini flight, and a flawless five-hour performance gave assurance that an astronaut can work successfully in space.

NASA

Astronaut Ed White, secured to Gemini 4, walks in space during the third orbit of the Gemini-Titan 4 flight.

Edward H. White II, in Gemini 4, conducted the first American EVA when he floated for twenty-one minutes in space and operated the space gun. In the manner of a gas station attendant, he cleaned the spacecraft's windshield and checked its thrusters.

Eugene Cernan, in Gemini 9, found his workload heavier than expected. His visor fogged up, and he had to end the space walk before he could test a backpack.

Michael Collins, in Gemini 10, used a space gun to propel himself to an Agena Target Vehicle and recover an attached meteorite-collection experiment. However, this EVA was terminated early because the spacecraft had used up the propellant supply allotted for the EVA.

Richard Gordon, in Gemini 11, had to use 80 per cent of his energy just to keep from floating away and to keep his arms and hands in front of him while hooking Gemini 11 to an Agena target vehicle with a rope. On earth, this task took him twenty-five seconds; in space, it required almost thirty minutes. The resulting perspiration and high level of fatigue caused the EVA to be cut short.

Edwin E. Aldrin, Jr., in Gemini 12, reversed the story of EVA troubles. He had new equipment—a portable handrail and golden, heat-reflecting slippers to keep him in place as he worked. He also had a new pattern for pacing himself, and took frequent two-minute rests. Aldrin therefore experienced no difficulty in carrying out such basic tasks as turning bolts, cutting cables, and plugging in electrical connections.

F-1. The most powerful U.S. liquid-fueled engine, developing 1.5 million pounds of thrust. Built by the Rocketdyne Division of North American Rockwell, the F-1 is installed in a cluster of five as the first stage of the Saturn 5 launch vehicle. It burns RP-1, a kerosene-like fuel, and liquid oxygen. One hundred and six of these engines have been ordered for use in Saturn 5 rockets.

Faith 7. The Mercury spacecraft which astronaut L. Gordon Cooper piloted for twenty-two orbits on May 15–16, 1963, in the concluding mission of Project Mercury. Because the automatic stabilization system failed to operate, Cooper controlled Faith 7 manually upon re-entry and landing. He set his craft down only 4.4 miles from the recovery carrier, the USS *Kearsarge,* near Midway Island in the Pacific Ocean.

federal space programs. Six U.S. agencies expend funds on space programs—three more than in 1960. The heaviest spending has shifted from the military to the civilian National Aeronautics and Space administration.

EXPENDITURES BY AGENCY
(In Millions of Dollars)

	1960	1968 (est.)
NASA	329*	5,190*
Department of Defense	518	1,840
Atomic Energy Commission	41	152
Department of Commerce	0	40
Department of the Interior	0	5
National Science Foundation	0	2

* Excludes amounts for aircraft technology.
SOURCE: Statistical Abstract of the United States

Flight Research Center. NASA installation at Edwards, Cal., adjoining Edwards Air Force Base, 65 miles northeast of Los Angeles. In support of Project Apollo, the Flight Research Center simulated moon landings and takeoffs to investigate possible operational and piloting problems. The center's most dramatic research revolved about the X-15 research rocket plane, an Air Force–Navy–NASA undertaking. One X-15 test investigates the possibility of returning from space by landing as an airplane.

food. Astronauts eat both rehydratable and bite-sized food during space flights. With a special gun, they inject water into such rehydratables (dry food items that can be reconstituted) as soup, pudding, salad, and beverage. The bite-sized food usually consists of a serving of six pieces, and it requires no rehydration. The meals are wrapped individually in aluminum foil and a polyethylene-polamide laminate.

The Gemini 7 astronauts, Frank Borman and James Lovell, Jr., had four different daily menus available during their fourteen-day flight. One of the menus—used on the second, sixth, tenth, and fourteenth days—follows:

MEAL A

	Calories
*Grapefruit drink	83
*Chicken and gravy	92
Beef sandwiches (6 pieces)	268
*Applesauce	165
Peanut cubes (6)	297
	905

MEAL B

*Orange-grapefruit drink	83
*Beef pot roast	119
Bacon and egg bites	206
*Chocolate pudding	307
	715

MEAL C

*Potato soup	220
*Shrimp cocktail	119
Date fruitcake	262
*Orange drink	83
	684
Total calories	2,304
Total weight	518.62 grams

* Rehydratable

Pillsbury Co. and Swift and Co. served as principal food contractors for the Gemini program. The U.S. Army Laboratory developed the food formulation concept, and Whirlpool Corp. handled the procurement, processing, and packaging.

footprint (colloquial). The full extent of the ocean area, roughly the shape of a foot, in which a returning spacecraft is capable of touching down for recovery. By using the lift capability built into the Apollo command module, a crew can "fly" to a point inside a footprint as large as 230 by 1,380 miles.

Freedom 7. The Mercury spacecraft in which Alan B. Shepard, Jr., made the first American flight into space. Launched by a Redstone rocket, Freedom 7 followed a ballistic path—as if fired from a gun—and stayed aloft for 15 minutes, 22 seconds, on May 5, 1961. It attained a maximum height of 116 miles and a maximum speed of 5,134 mph before splashing down in the Atlantic Ocean about 500 miles northwest of Grand Turk Island—a distance of 302 miles down-range. Freedom 7 afforded its astronaut less visibility than its successors, for it had only a 33-square-inch viewport on either side. Later Mercury spacecraft had a 209-square-inch window giving an astronaut a direct line of sight. Freedom 7 is now on display in the Smithsonian Institution, Washington, D.C.

Friendship 7. The spacecraft piloted by John H. Glenn, Jr., in the free world's first orbital flight. Launched on Feb. 20, 1962, by an Atlas vehicle, Friendship 7 circled the earth three times at altitudes of from 100 to 162 miles. It stayed aloft 4 hours, 55 minutes, 23 seconds before splashing down about 160 miles east of Grand Turk Island. Friendship 7 traveled 80,969 miles and reached a maximum speed of 17,544 mph.

Glenn's craft made its epic journey three years and thirty-nine days after McDonnell Aircraft was given a contract for the nation's first set of manned spacecraft. It measured nearly 11 feet, 1 inch in length and exactly 6 feet, 2.5 inches in width.

fuel (rocket). See *propellants*.

fuel cell. A device in which gaseous hydrogen and oxygen are combined chemically to give electricity, water, and heat. Fuel cells are desirable for space flight because they weigh less than conventional batteries.

Fuel cells withstood a severe test when they performed beyond expectations throughout the fourteen-day flight of Gemini 7—their second test in manned space flight. Trouble developed in the oxygen heating system of the fuel cells in the Gemini 5 mission, in which they were introduced, but that mission was able to go its full seven days through careful use of electrical power.

The two fuel cells in a Gemini spacecraft weigh 68 pounds each, and each consists of three stacks of thirty-two individual cells. The reactants—hydrogen and oxygen stored at cryogenic temperatures—are forced into the stacks and are changed chemically by an electrolyte of polymer plastic and a catalyst of platinum. The electrons and ions that result combine with oxygen to form electricity (used directly for power), water (diverted to supply tanks), and heat (rejected by the spacecraft coolant system). It is a controlled reaction that continues as long as fuel and oxidant are supplied. General Electric makes the fuel cells.

fuel sloshing. In rocketry, the movement of fuel away from tank outlets under weightless conditions. Liquid hydrogen presents a particularly difficult problem after an upper stage has been fired, coasts in orbit, and then attempts to restart. Weightless during the coasting stage, the fuel tends to slosh or float free in the partly empty tank, putting it out of position for flowing to the engines. NASA engineers are seeking the best ways to position propellants over tank outlets during restart. Simultaneously, they are conducting research on keeping the fuels from escaping through vent valves during the coasting stage.

G, g, or **G-force.** A unit of measure of gravity. One *g* equals the gravitational pull required to move a body at the rate of about 32.2 feet per second per second; that is, the body undergoing an acceleration of one *g* will increase in velocity 32.2 feet per second during each second. The stress undergone by astronauts during acceleration is measured in *g*'s, and particular attention is given to G-forces during launching and re-entry. See *acceleration*.

gantry. See *service tower*.

Gemini (project). Project Gemini, the second phase of the U.S. manned space-flight program (Dec. 7, 1961–Nov. 15, 1966), put astronauts into orbit two by two to carry out advanced missions requiring the ability to maneuver their spacecraft. Having advanced from the "man-in-the-can" days of Project Mercury in which a pilot simply orbited the earth and observed, Project Gemini employed second-generation spacecraft. The Gemini spacecraft were under the full control of the astronauts and could be guided from one orbital plane to another.

Dr. Robert R. Gilruth, director of NASA's Manned Spacecraft Center, summed up the accomplishments of the Gemini flights: "We had to learn how to maneuver with high precision, to make rendezvous, to dock, to light off large propulsion systems in space, to work outside in the hard vacuum of outer space. We had to learn how man could endure long durations in the weightless environment. We had to learn how to make precise landings from orbit."

The project dates from Dec. 7, 1961, when NASA announced plans to develop a two-man spacecraft, with McDonnell Aircraft as the manufacturer. It was not until almost a month later—Jan. 3, 1962—that NASA announced that the project would be called Gemini, after the constellation containing the twin stars Castor and Pollux. The Martin Company's Titan 2, a U.S. Air Force missile, was modified to become the standard launch vehicle. For rendezvous and docking missions, NASA used Lockheed's Agena target vehicle, placed in orbit by General Dynamics' Atlas standard launch vehicle. The first Gemini spacecraft—unmanned— was flown in 1964, and a series of spectacular manned flights followed in 1965 and 1966.

Project Gemini was directed by the Office of Manned Space Flight, NASA Headquarters, and managed by NASA's Manned Spacecraft Center. The U.S. Department of Defense participated in booster development, launch operations, tracking, and recovery.

The first rendezvous, Gemini 7 photographed from Gemini 6.

A summary of the Gemini missions:

Gemini 1 (Apr. 8, 1964). Unmanned mission. Spacecraft and second-stage launch vehicle orbited about four days to test performance. No recovery attempted.

Gemini 2 (Jan. 19, 1965). Unmanned ballistic flight. Qualified the re-entry heat protection system and other spacecraft systems. Gemini 2 recovered from the Atlantic Ocean.

Gemini 3 (Mar. 23, 1965). Grissom, now a major as he became the first man to fly into space a second time, and Lt. Comdr. John W. Young, Navy, made three orbits in 4 hours, 53 minutes. The first manned spacecraft to change orbital plane in flight; maneuvered by firing small rockets, called thrusters.

Gemini 4 (June 3–7, 1965). Maj. James A. McDivitt and Maj. Edward H. White II, both of the Air Force, completed 62 revolutions in 4 days, 1 hour, 59 minutes. On the third revolution White opened an overhead hatch and floated out to take a 21-minute "space walk" 103 miles above the earth. In this extravehicular activity, White propelled himself with a hand-held maneuvering unit—virtually a Buck Rogers rocket gun.

Gemini 5 (Aug. 21–29, 1965). Cooper, a lieutenant colonel on his second orbital flight, and Lt. Comdr. Charles (Pete) Conrad, Jr., Navy, completed 120 revolutions covering 3.3 million miles in 7 days, 22 hours, 56 minutes. On the first day the oxygen heating system in the fuel cell supply system failed. However, the full mission was completed by careful use of electrical power and excellent operational management of fuel cells.

Gemini 7 (Dec. 4–18, 1965). Maj: Frank Borman, Air Force, and Lt. Comdr. James A. Lovell, Jr., Navy, completed 206 revolutions covering 5.7 million miles in 13 days, 18 hours, 35 minutes. As the nation watched them on live television, Borman and Lovell climbed out of their recovery helicopter and walked across the deck of the carrier USS *Wasp* in a rubber-legged gait—but both were physically fit after man's toughest space flight. Gemini 7 removed a lingering— even though slight—doubt that man could remain in the hostile environment of space for fourteen days.

Astronauts James Lovell and Frank Borman after completing 14-day space mission in the Gemini 7 spacecraft.

Gemini 6 (Dec. 15–16, 1965). Schirra, now a captain on his second flight, and Maj. Thomas P. Stafford, Air Force, completed 15 revolutions in 1 day, 1 hour, 51 minutes. On Dec. 15, the Gemini 6 spacecraft overtook the Gemini 7 spacecraft in the latter's established orbit, and in history's first space rendezvous the two met nose to nose about twelve inches apart, 185 miles above the earth.

Contrary to original plans, Gemini 6 lifted off later than Gemini 7. The first delay came on Oct. 25, when the Agena was destroyed by a hard start of its primary propulsion system. Another delay followed on Dec. 12, when an electrical plug connecting the Gemini launch vehicle with the pad electrical system dropped out, shutting down the engines slightly more than a second after ignition.

Gemini 8 (Mar. 16, 1966). Neil A. Armstrong, civilian,

and Maj. David R. Scott, Air Force, in a flight of 10 hours, 42 minutes, achieved the first docking of two spacecraft in earth orbit. They linked up with an Agena target vehicle placed in orbit about 100 minutes earlier. However, a roll thruster on their craft began firing continuously because of an electrical short circuit. Armstrong and Scott undocked from the Agena and used the re-entry control system to regain control. They landed in the Pacific Ocean on the seventh revolution.

Gemini 9 (June 3–6, 1966). Stafford, now a lieutenant colonel on his second flight, and Lt. Comdr. Eugene A. Cernan, Navy, completed 44 revolutions in 72 hours, 20 minutes. They made three separate rendezvous with an Augmented Target Docking Adapter. In addition, Cernan worked and floated for two hours and ten minutes outside the cabin, in what NASA calls "extravehicular activity."

Gemini 10 (July 18–21, 1966). Young, now a Navy commander on his second flight, and Maj. Michael Collins, Air Force, orbited for 70 hours, 47 minutes. They docked with their Agena target vehicle, used the Agena engine to rise to a record altitude of 476 miles, and made a rendezvous with the lifeless Agena that had been launched for Gemini 8. Collins also made one space walk and one stand-up maneuver with the hatch open.

Gemini 11 (Sep. 12–15, 1966). Conrad, now a commander, and Lt. Comdr. Richard F. Gordon, Jr., Navy, achieved a rendezvous and docked with an Agena target vehicle on the first revolution. They later ignited the Agena's propulsion system and drove the docked vehicles to an altitude of 850 miles. They conducted extravehicular activity twice. They tethered the Gemini 11 to the Agena at a height of 185 miles in a "station-keeping" exercise to save spacecraft maneuvering fuel while keeping two orbiting space vehicles close together. For the first time, an on-board computer controlled a landing by handling guidance and firing the maneuvering rockets.

Gemini 12 (Nov. 11–15, 1966). Lovell, now a captain, and Maj. Edwin E. Aldrin, Jr., Air Force, closed the Gemini program with an impressive display of extravehicular activity.

Aldrin made three EVA excursions—one a walk outside and two standing in his seat—lasting a total of 5 hours, 37 minutes. Moreover, by working at a planned pace with frequent rests, he experienced no exertion difficulties such as others had encountered in EVA. Rendezvous and docking with an Agena were achieved on the third revolution, as planned. A computer-controlled landing put Gemini 12 into the Atlantic within sight of the USS *Wasp*.

The Gemini spacecraft consisted of two major units—the re-entry module and the adapter module—which together weighed seven thousand pounds at launch. Just before return to the earth's atmosphere, the two-man crew jettisoned the adapter module, and only the 4,700-pound re-entry module splashed down into the ocean.

A bigger, heavier, and more sophisticated successor to the Mercury, the complete Gemini spacecraft was 18 feet, 5 inches in length. Conical in shape, it measured 10 feet in diameter at its widest part and narrowed to 39 inches at the top. The Gemini, unlike the Mercury, could change to another orbit, and it incorporated support systems able to sustain life for more than two weeks.

Re-entry module. It is 11 feet high and 7.5 feet in diameter at its base and consists of a rendezvous and recovery (R&R) section, a re-entry control section (RCS), the crew compartment or cabin, and the heat shield.

1. Rendezvous and recovery section. Contains radar for rendezvous and the drogue, pilot, and main parachutes for recovery. Located in the narrow forward end of the spacecraft.

2. Re-entry control section. Carries fuel and oxidizer tanks, valves, tubing, and two systems of attitude-control thrusters to permit control of the re-entry module from retrograde to deployment of the main parachute. The identical but separate systems consist of eight fixed-mount thrusters operating on storable hypergolic propellants. Should one system fail, the other still can control attitude. Use of attitude-control jets enables the astronauts to lengthen or shorten the descent to fly to a selected landing point.

3. Cabin section. A pressurized hull that is 85 per cent

(by weight) welded titanium assemblies. It houses two astronauts, seated side by side, and also systems connected directly with the crew. These systems include the three main instrument and control panels, guidance controls, the environmental control system, and ejection seats similar to those in fighter aircraft. Equipment that does not require a pressurized environment is kept between the pressurized hull and the outer shell. The dish-shaped heat shield is attached to the large end of the re-entry module.

Adapter module. It is 7.5 feet high and 10 feet in diameter across its base and consists of an equipment section and a retrograde section.

1. Equipment section. Contains fuel for the orbit attitude maneuvering system, primary oxygen for the environmental control system, and electrical power source systems. It also serves as a radiator for the cooling system.

2. Retrograde section. Contains four solid-propellant retrograde rockets, each with 2,500 pounds of thrust. They are symmetrically mounted about the longitudinal axis of the spacecraft. Fired in sequence, the rockets slow down the spacecraft and permit it to start re-entry into the earth's atmosphere.

The adapter module is jettisoned in two steps: (a) the equipment section is discarded immediately before the retrorockets are fired for re-entry; (b) the retrograde section is dropped after the retrorockets are fired.

McDonnell Aircraft was prime contractor for the Gemini spacecraft. Other contractors were AiResearch, environmental control; General Electric, fuel cell; Honeywell, all-inertial guidance; IBM, guidance computer; Rocketdyne, re-entry control; Thiokol Chemical, retrorocket system; Westinghouse, rendezvous radar.

geodesy. The science that deals with the size and shape of the the earth. Geodesy centers on earth measurement. Before the advent of artificial satellites, difficulty was encountered in surveying hard-to-cross mountains, deserts, and vast expanses of water. In the 1960's, geodesy is advanced through use of geodetic satellites, which cover the entire earth regardless of oceans and difficult terrain and obtain better geodetic data than could be gained by traditional means. Geodetic satellites: (1) supply a triangulation point in space to help determine exact positions and distances on earth; (2) use gravimetric techniques—measuring variations of the earth's gravitational field. GEOS, PAGEOS, SECOR, and ANNA 1B are geodetic satellites.

An early satellite, Vanguard 1, contributed to geodesy in 1959. Its stability of orbit provided geodetic observations, one of which was the determination that the geoid—the shape of the earth at sea level—is slightly pear-shaped.

Geodetic Earth-Orbiting Satellite (GEOS). A satellite program which marked its first flight in 1965 when GEOS 1 (Explorer 29) was launched into an orbit 692 by 1,414 miles. Later launches will make detailed studies of the gravitational field of the earth under the U.S. Geodetic Satellite Program. The 385-pound GEOS, built by the Applied Physics Laboratory, carries four flashing lights, laser reflectors, and radio tracking beacons.

GEOS 2 (Explorer 36) was launched aboard a Delta rocket from the Western Test Range, Cal., on Jan. 11, 1968.

GGS. See *gravity gradient stabilization.*

gimbal. "Mechanical frame containing two mutually perpendicular intersecting axes of rotation (bearings and/or shafts)."—(Air Force)

Many rocket engines, such as the outer engines in a cluster of five, are gimbal-mounted to provide directional control and stability. The engines may be tilted to direct the rocket exhaust to "steer" the whole launch vehicle.

Glenn, John H., Jr. The first American to orbit the earth. His three-orbit flight on Feb. 20, 1962, made the Marine colonel a symbol of the nation's capabilities in space, and his honors included an invitation to address a joint session of the U.S. Senate and House of Representatives. He was born on July 18, 1921, in Cambridge, Ohio, and grew up in nearby New Concord, where he attended Muskingum College. Glenn flew 59 combat missions in the Pacific theater in World War II and 63 more missions in the Korean conflict, where he shot down three planes. He gained national attention even before becoming a Mercury astronaut by setting a transcontinental speed record (averaging 726 mph) in a Crusader jet in 1957. Glenn retired from the service in 1965, and he is now a director of Royal Crown Cola Company and a NASA consultant.

glitch (colloquial). A mistake or foul-up. Usually it is attributable to inanimate things rather than persons.

Goddard, Dr. Robert H. (1882–1945). American physicist who launched the world's first liquid-fueled rocket and developed fundamental theories of rocketry that opened the way for today's launch vehicles. Dr. Goddard, a professor of physics at Clark University in Massachusetts, fired his first rocket 184 feet at Auburn, Mass., on Mar. 16, 1926. Three years later he scored another "first" with an instrumented rocket. It carried a thermometer and a barometer, along with a small camera that recorded their readings at peak altitude. By 1935, in Roswell, N.M., his rockets reached speeds of more than 700 mph and altitudes of more than 7,500 feet. Dr. Goddard's work received financial support from the Smithsonian Institution (which also published two of his papers) and from the Daniel and Florence Guggenheim Foundation. In World War II he served as director of research for the Navy's Bureau of Aeronautics.

Goddard Space Flight Center. NASA installation covering 550 acres in Greenbelt, Md., a northeast suburb of Washington, D.C. The center is named for Dr. Robert H. Goddard, rocket pioneer. Goddard develops and manages scores of programs for earth-orbiting satellites, designs and tests NASA sounding rockets, and serves as a nerve center for global communications linking NASA tracking stations.

Goddard receives more than 55 million data points daily from its orbiting observatories, Explorer spacecraft, and weather and communications satellites in orbit—so much data that storage requires more than 100,000 reels of magnetic tape annually.

During manned missions, Goddard's computing equipment processes tracking information as events occur ("real time") around the world. Before launch and during intervals when a manned spacecraft is out of range of a specific station, Goddard also makes a system-by-system, station-by-station, computer-programmed checkout to certify the network's readiness. This is known as CADFISS (Computation and Data Flow Integrated Subsystem).

Goddard operates five laboratories in separate buildings—research projects, space sciences, satellite systems, instrument contruction and installation, and flight control and range operations. It also has separate buildings devoted to space projects and payload testing.

Goldstone "210." A parabolic aluminum-dish reflector 210 feet in diameter, the world's largest and most sensitive automatic space-tracking antenna, placed in use in 1966 at Goldstone, Cal., in the Mojave Desert. The dish covers an area of almost an acre and stands as tall as a twenty-one-story building.

The "210" has the ability to follow future spacecraft to the planet Pluto at the outer limits of the solar system. It makes possible far more distant tracking than the standard 85-foot antennas, and quickly proved its value by tracking Pioneer 6 in its orbit around the sun, extending the useful life of Pioneer 6 by about a year.

The giant antenna is able to collect deep-space signals so weak that their energy measures one-billionth of one-billionth of one watt. These signals are maser-amplified about forty thousand times and fed into the receiver, where they are amplified further. Existence of the "210" will enhance space exploration by enabling spacecraft designers to use equipment that will send back data in greater quantities and with greater precision.

Rohr Corporation, builder of the antenna, reported that the five-million-pound rotating weight of the giant dish is carried on a pressurized film of oil on a 77-foot hydrostatic bearing. Despite its size, the dish can move from horizontal to vertical in three minutes. See *antennas*.

gravitation. The attraction or pull that all particles of matter have for each other. The law of gravitation, formulated by Sir Isaac Newton in 1687, applies to man-made vehicles moving in space just as it applies to the planets and makes their movements predictable. Newton's law says that any two bodies in the universe attract each other with a force that varies "directly as to the product of their masses and inversely as the square of the distance between them." A larger body has a stronger gravitational pull; the closer two bodies are to each other, the greater the gravitation is. An Apollo spacecraft traveling to the moon would be subject to the gravitational pulls of the earth, the moon, and the sun.

gravity gradient stabilization (GGS). A method by which an object in space is stabilized in orbit by equal pulls of gravity and centrifugal force. The typical GGS satellite is given an elongated shape, something like a lopsided barbell. One end sinks toward earth; the other is tugged toward space. The Air Force, Navy, and NASA all have experimented with versions of the GGS, which eliminates the need for firing short bursts of fuel to control attitude. Gemini 11 experimented with the gravity gradient principle by tethering itself to an Agena target vehicle. In that position, the Gemini 11 engaged in "station keeping"—maintaining an established position—without using fuel to correct its attitude.

gyroscope. A spinning body mounted in gimbals. It helps to guide flight in space. For example, the inertial guidance system in the Gemini spacecraft had three gyroscopes to stabilize and orient the stable platform. See *inertial guidance system*.

H

H–1. An engine built by North American Rockwell's Rocketdyne Division. The H–1 is used in a cluster of eight engines as the first stage in both the Saturn 1 and the Uprated Saturn 1 launch vehicles. In the latter vehicle, each of the eight H–1's is rated at 200,000 pounds of thrust, for a total thrust of 1.6 million pounds. Together, the eight engines burn for about 2.5 minutes and carry the Uprated Saturn 1 to an altitude of 37 miles before engine cutoff. In that time the engines burn 41,000 gallons (270,000 pounds) of RP-1 fuel and 66,000 gallons (615,000 pounds) of liquid oxygen.

Ham. A 37-pound chimpanzee who flew 155 miles high and a distance of 420 miles down the Atlantic aboard a Mercury spacecraft on Jan. 31, 1961. Ham reacted normally to prolonged weightlessness and was recovered unharmed from the ocean. His journey helped open the way to the first manned suborbital flight in Project Mercury by Alan Shepard on May 5 of that year. On Nov. 29 Ham orbited the earth twice as a prelude to America's first orbital flight, by John Glenn, in 1962.

hand-held maneuvering unit (HHMU). A "space gun" used by an astronaut in a "space walk." Using nitrogen as a fuel, the unit gives the astronaut positive control of his direction and propels him from place to place in the weightless environment of space. The unit weighs 3.5 pounds. The fuel is kept in bottles in the spacecraft and is fed to the unit through the umbilical.

hardware (colloquial). Manufactured equipment, such as a spacecraft or launch vehicle, or equipment used in either, such as a propellant tank or an on-board computer. It is a useful bit of jargon in that "hardware" quickly distinguishes physical equipment from missions.

heat shield. A device that protects a spacecraft from heat. The shield on the blunt end of the Gemini craft, for example, protects it against temperatures that rise to 3,000° F during re-entry into the earth's atmosphere at 16,450 mph.

The Apollo command module has a wrap-around heat shield consisting of three pieces that cover the top (apex), sides, and blunt end. The craft's outer structure is brazed honeycomb steel, to which is bonded an epoxy resin ablative material. The thickness of the ablative material varies from 0.9 to 2.6 inches, depending upon the heat anticipated in various areas. Avco, maker of the Apollo shield, reported that it would protect astronauts against temperatures ranging from minus 200° to more than 5,000° F.

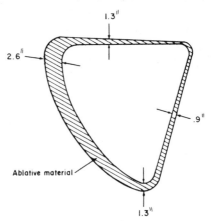

NASA

Early studies have indicated that a Mars craft would need a heat shield about 3.5 inches thick to withstand re-entry heat of 35,000° F at speeds up to 44,000 mph.

When a returning spacecraft encounters the same "fireball" effect as a natural meteor, a heat shield guards it in these ways: (1) a charring ablative material begins to decompose chemically, and absorbs some heat in the process; (2) during decomposition, gases are evolved and dilute the hot air over the shield surface; (3) a charred layer of coke-like material develops, and it radiates the heat away from the craft; and (4) the uncharred inner layers insulate the craft.

HHMU. See *hand-held maneuvering unit.*

HL-10 (for "horizontal landing" and tenth concept of its type). A manned research vehicle of the wingless lifting body class. It has a flat bottom, rounded top, and half-conical design. There are three angled vertical fins at the rear.

    Length: 24 ft.
    Width: 10 ft.
    Height: 8 ft.
    Weight: 5,000 lbs.

The HL-10 made its first glide flight in December 1966, and engineers then redesigned its tail fin to improve control. A series of test flights was scheduled for 1968.

    The HL-10 is built by Martin Co., a division of Martin Marietta Corp., for the Aeronautical Systems Division of the Air Force Systems Command. See *lifting body.*

hold. A halt in a countdown. It stops the sequence of events so that a difficulty can be removed.

hydrogen, liquid. See *liquid hydrogen.*

hypergolic fuel. Fuel that ignites spontaneously upon contact with an oxidizer. Hypergolic fuel eliminates the need for an ignition system. Titan 2 uses such a fuel—a 50–50 blend of monomethyl hydrazine and unsymmetrical-dimethyl hydrazine (UDMH). Its oxidizer is nitrogen tetroxide.

ICBM. See *intercontinental ballistic missile.*

ICBM Alarm. A series of Air Force polar-orbiting satellites, designed to detect enemy firings of intercontinental ballistic missiles. The program was formerly called MIDAS, and in 1960 and 1961 the Air Force announced four launchings. Since that time details have been secret.

IDCSP. See *Initial Defense Communications Satellite Program.*

IMP. Interplanetary Monitoring Platform. See *Explorer.*

inclination. As a descriptive feature of an orbit: the angle between the plane of an earth satellite's orbit and the plane of the earth's equator. Gemini 7 had a 32° inclination to the earth's equator; ESSA 2, flying virtually from the North Pole to the South Pole, had a 100.98° inclination.

In astronomy: the inclination of a planet is the angle between the ecliptic (the plane of the earth's orbit) and the plane of the planet's orbit. Pluto's orbit is inclined more than 17° to the ecliptic, or far more than that of any other planet.

inertial guidance system. A system, based on the laws of inertia, that enables a spacecraft to determine its own position and to supply information that can be used to guide it. Inertial guidance is based on the tendency of motionless objects to remain motionless, and the tendency of moving objects to stay in motion unless some external force acts upon them. Gyroscopes and accelerometers measure those forces.

Honeywell, Inc., builder of the Gemini inertial guidance system, explained: "The accelerometers, mounted on a stable platform that can automatically level itself and keep itself pointed in a fixed direction, measure changes in acceleration. The platform does this with the aid of precision gyroscopes— spinning wheels that maintain a constant plane of rotation. A

Centaur inertial reference sensors are tightly packaged in this inertial platform azimuth-block (inner gimbal) at Honeywell's Aeronautical Division.

clock tells how long the acceleration forces were exerted, and from that it is possible for a computer to calculate speed and distance traveled. The Gemini inertial guidance system has three gyroscopes to stabilize and orient the stable platform and three accelerometers to measure the changes of speed in three dimensions (roll, pitch, and yaw). A computer uses the information provided to calculate position and generate signals to steer the spacecraft to a desired position or track."

infrared. Pertaining to radiation beyond the red end of the visible spectrum. Infrared radiation is radiant heat, such as that from an electric iron.

Initial Defense Communications Satellite Program (IDCSP). A Department of Defense global communications system, based on random satellites that circle the earth around the equator at altitudes of from 18,100 to 18,600 miles. At that level, each satellite is nearly synchronous; that is, it travels at about the speed of the earth and thus in effect hovers over a spot. This "initial" system is a research and development setup leading to a future "advanced" DCSP.

The IDCSP got off to a big-scale beginning in 1966 when a single Air Force Titan 3–C launch vehicle inserted seven of the satellites into orbit simultaneously, along with one gravity-gradient test satellite. Voice communications were established immediately between the U.S. East and West Coasts, and the U.S. East Coast and Europe.

In July 1967, the IDCSP was declared operational for the Pacific area. It consisted of 25 orbiting satellites as well as Army-developed ground terminals in Hawaii, the Philippines, and South Vietnam. The Air Force said that traffic between Hawaii and Saigon exceeded 1,000 calls per week.

Intelsat (satellite and consortium). The name of a second-generation communications satellite (after Early Bird) and also the name of the satellite's owner, the 54-nation International Telecommunications Satellite Consortium. The Communications Satellite Corp. is the U.S. representative and manager of the consortium. The satellite Intelsat 2, placed over the Pacific Ocean in 1966, was also known as Lani Bird. Lani is Hawaiian for "heavenly."

Using Delta rockets, NASA launched three Intelsats for Comsat from Cape Kennedy in 1967.

Integrate-Transfer-Launch (ITL) Facility. An installation at Cape Kennedy to permit assembly and checkout of Titan 3 vehicles off the launching pads. ITL gives Titan 3 what the Air Force calls "quick responsiveness"—the capability of high launch rates from fewer pads. The installation consists of an integration building (where booster stages and payloads are put together), control center, solid assembly building (where solid rockets are strapped on), mobile service tower, mobile vans containing electronic checkout equipment, and launch pad.

intercontinental ballistic missile (ICBM). A missile—that is, a military weapon—"with a range of more than 3,000 miles," by definition of the Joint Chiefs of Staff. The next smaller classification is intermediate range ballistic missile (IRBM).

The aerospace industry categorizes its fields as aircraft,

space, and missiles, and therefore the ICBM and IRBM lie outside the direct interest of space flight. However, the development of the technology and hardware for these missiles, which began in the 1950's, made possible the powerful launch vehicles of the 1960's.

The Atlas and Titan ICBM's were modified to become launch vehicles bearing the same names. The comparatively small Redstone—once deployed in Europe as a weapon—evolved into today's giant Saturn vehicles. The Thor, originally an IRBM, evolved into today's Thor and Delta launch vehicles.

A different kind of ICBM, the solid-fueled Minuteman, has not been converted into a standard launch vehicle for space uses. Smaller, lighter, and simpler than the liquid-fueled vehicles, the Minuteman, because of its solid propulsion, has the military advantage of always being ready for firing.

interferometer. "An apparatus used to produce and measure interference from two or more coherent wave trains from the same source. Interferometers are used to measure wave lengths, to measure angular width of sources, to determine the angular position of sources (as in satellite tracking), and for many other purposes."—(NASA)

Interplanetary Explorer. See *Explorer.*

Interplanetary Monitoring Platform (IMP). See *Explorer.*

interplanetary space. Space between the planets. Other subdivisions of outer space—as distances grow progressively greater—are interstellar space (between the stars) and intergalactic space (between the galaxies).

ion propulsion. Propulsion by ion rocket engines, which obtain thrust by electrical acceleration of charged particles. (An "ion" is an atom or molecularly bound group of atoms having an electric charge.)

Ion propulsion is still in the early stages of development, but it has given indications of advantages (when used after chemical or other rockets have boosted a spacecraft above the atmosphere). Although ion engines develop little thrust, they can accelerate a spacecraft gradually to great velocity in an airless, weightless environment.

In 1964 NASA tested two ion rocket engines in a spacecraft called SERT 1 (for Space Electric Rocket Test). One was the electron-bombardment type, using vaporized ions of mercury as its fuel. This engine, developed by NASA's Lewis Research Center, ran for thirty minutes in space. The second engine, developed by Hughes Research Laboratories for the Lewis Center, was a contact-ionization type using cesium as a fuel. It did not run during the SERT 1 test.

Ion engines offer the possibility of supplying power for long periods—possibly long enough to propel a spacecraft to the limits of the solar system. In 1966 an electric engine was operated nonstop for 341 days in a space simulation center at Electro-Optical Systems, Inc. This was the longest continuous test of any U.S. space thruster system. The engine was of the electron-bombardment type, in which high voltages are used to accelerate the propellant (cesium) which has been previously ionized by electrons emitted from a cathode. The Lewis Research Center, for which the test was performed, reported that the specific impulse was 5,010 seconds. The average thrust during the test was 7.07 millipounds—seven one-thousandths of a pound.

ionosphere. "The region of the atmosphere, above roughly 70 kilometers [43 miles] which is sufficiently ionized to affect the propagation of radio signals. It overlaps the mesosphere and the thermosphere. It is usually divided into the D (70–85 km), E (85–140 km), F1 (140–200 km), and the F2 (above 200 km) layers, which differ in the density of ions, and the dominant ionic species. Radio waves longer in wavelength than a few tens of meters will be reflected by the ionosphere."—(American Institute of Physics)

ITL Facility. See *Integrate-Transfer-Launch Facility.*

J-2. A liquid-hydrogen-fueled engine built by the Rocketdyne Division of North American Rockwell. It is the top (second) stage of the Uprated Saturn 1 and also the top (third) stage of the Saturn 5, providing the final velocity increment to put an Apollo spacecraft into orbit. Each J-2 develops a thrust of about 200,000 pounds (although it may vary from 175,000 to 225,000 pounds in different phases of flight).

Jet Propulsion Laboratory (JPL). A government-owned laboratory at Pasadena, Cal., operated by the California Institute of Technology under contract to NASA. JPL became well known to the American public when its picture-taking spacecraft scored successes in the mid-1960's—Mariner 4 that flew by Mars; the Rangers that impacted on the moon; and the Surveyor, which landed softly on the moon on its first attempt. In addition to performing research and development work on lunar and interplanetary programs, JPL develops and operates deep-space tracking facilities.

Jodrell Bank. The site in Britain where the University of Manchester operates a 250-foot-diameter, fully steerable antenna used for radio astronomy. The Jodrell Bank antenna tracks American and Soviet spacecraft millions of miles from the earth.

JPL. See *Jet Propulsion Laboratory.*

Jupiter (missile). An intermediate-range ballistic missile developed from the Redstone and used as a space booster. See *Redstone.*

Jupiter (planet). The largest planet in the solar system, with a diameter about eleven times that of the earth. Jupiter's brilliancy is exceeded only by that of Venus among the planets, and it has a dozen moons. However, Jupiter's distance from the earth is so vast—varying from 367 to 599 million miles—that planetary exploration now centers on the closer planets, Venus and Mars.

Kennedy Space Center (KSC). NASA's John F. Kennedy Space Center, on Florida's east coast, just north of launch facilities formerly shared with the military at Cocoa Beach. The spaceport is responsible for the assembling, checking out, and launching of vehicles. NASA launch complexes handle Apollo/Saturn 5, Apollo/Uprated Saturn 1, Atlas-Centaur, Atlas-Agena, and Delta vehicles.

Complex 39, built on Merritt Island in the mid-1960's, has become the nation's "moon port," the home of Apollo/Saturn 5. Complex 39 is dominated by the Vehicle Assembly Building, the world's largest building, as tall as a fifty-two-story skyscraper and nearly as spacious as the Pentagon and Chicago's Merchandise Mart combined. Two six-million-pound crawlers, or transporters, the world's largest land vehicles, also serve the complex. Each crawler is able to carry both a Saturn 5 rocket and a mobile launcher (of which there are three) from the Vertical Assembly Building to a launch pad. There are two octagonal concrete-and-steel stands—Pads A and B—as launch sites.

Kiwi. A nuclear reactor tested in development of a power plant for nuclear propulsion on space missions. The Kiwi was flightless, just like the New Zealand bird for which it was named. The Los Alamos Scientific Laboratory operated it by using the liquid hydrogen as a propellant and coolant, along with a liquid-hydrogen-cooled nozzle, which would be required in flight. On Aug. 28, 1964, at the NASA-Atomic Energy Commission test facility at Jackass Flats, Nev., the Kiwi B-4E reactor was operated for eight minutes at one thousand megawatts and ran free of dangerous vibration. The B-4E was the eighth and last Kiwi reactor built for testing; it was the land-based predecessor of the Nuclear Engine for Rocket Vehicle Application. See *NERVA* and *Rover*.

Laika (Russian for "barker"). The dog that rode into space in the USSR's Sputnik 2 on Nov. 3, 1957. She lived in space for about a week and then died, apparently from lack of oxygen.

Lani Bird. See *Intelsat.*

Langley Research Center. NASA installation at Hampton, Va., concentrating on research into materials, structures, and vehicle shapes in space flight, and also in aeronautics.

Much of Langley's space work concerns application of new materials and problems of re-entry, involving tests of lifting bodies. Among Langley's projects that will be of increasing interest in years ahead is the development of designs and techniques for using parachutes to land instrumented, unmanned capsules on Mars. The balloon-like Echo satellites and the Scout rocket—often used at nearby Wallops Island— were developed at Langley. The center includes forty wind tunnels and also heat-study equipment that can attain temperatures of 16,000° F.

laser (acronym for light amplification by stimulated emission of radiation). A device used to generate coherent light—that is, highly concentrated and organized beams of light. Laser light waves have been described as marching in step like soldiers. NASA has a long-range program to develop the technology to use lasers for communications and deep-space exploration. It has assigned Perkin-Elmer Corp. and Chrysler Corp. to do research into optical technology, including laser propagation studies.

The laser—a thin but powerful beam—holds the promise of great usefulness in space by carrying communications across vast distances with precise aim.

In 1967 engineers at the Air Force Avionics Laboratory, Wright-Patterson AFB, Ohio, sent voice transmissions over a laser beam six miles long. They used a pistol-shaped transmitter to aim the beam.

In 1968 NASA's Surveyor 7, sitting on the surface of the moon and taking pictures of the earth, photographed laser beams originating from two earth stations—at Tucson, Ariz., and Wrightwood, Cal. The beams originated when lasers were coupled to telescopes. The green argon ion laser beams were believed to be only a few miles wide when they reached the moon.

The Manned Spacecraft Center of NASA has expressed interest in developing laser tracking techniques between earth and a manned deep-space vehicle. The proposed system would handle two-way voice communications and telemetry and one-way spacecraft-to-earth television.

launch complex. A site and the equipment for launching spacecraft. For example, Launch Complex 36 at Cape Kennedy, the site of Atlas-Centaur launches, consists of Pads A and B, a common blockhouse, a launch and service building, service towers, and storage facilities for liquid hydrogen, liquid oxygen, RP-1, liquid and gaseous nitrogen, and helium.

launch pad. A concrete platform from which a rocket is launched. Costly associated equipment on the pad includes elaborate wiring for communications, a blast bucket (curved plate) to deflect flames, fire protection pumps, and equipment to weigh fuels as they are fed into the rocket. If a rocket falls and burns on a pad, damage may run into the millions of dollars.

launch umbilical tower. See *mobile launcher.*

launch vehicles. Devices that make space exploration possible by propelling spacecraft into earth orbit or by projecting them into trajectories toward other celestial bodies.

The launch vehicles carry aloft a spacecraft or some other payload (such as the large passive reflecting sphere called PAGEOS). Thus the largest U.S. launch vehicle of the 1960's, the Saturn 5, will carry aloft the Apollo spacecraft, and together they will form the Apollo/Saturn 5 space vehicle.

All launch vehicles so far have been chemical rockets to

put objects into orbit. Engines combine the turbine engine, the ramjet, and the rocket to save weight in producing the energy required to get into orbit. The advanced vehicles of the future may use other power plants once orbit is achieved. For example, a stream of molecules from an ion engine would propel a vehicle in space. For high energy, nuclear power has been talked about but has not been developed for space purposes.

The Fleet. To support the nation's space program, the National Aeronautics and Space Administration and the U.S. Air Force operate an assortment of launch vehicles that may be compared to a fleet of trucks. There are vehicles for light hauling, such as the slim Scout, which delivers a spacecraft or payload of a few hundred pounds into earth orbit. And there are heavy-duty vehicles for immense jobs, such as Saturn 5, which is being developed either to carry more than 140 tons into earth orbit or more than 45 tons on a moon journey.

Selection of a vehicle for a mission is based on the flight path desired for a specific spacecraft. Rocket engineers must calculate how much push (thrust) will be required, for how long (burning time), to carry a certain weight, and to give the spacecraft the exact velocity.

The number of basic launch vehicles is not as great as it appears at first glance. The relatively small Scout stands as the only U.S. launch vehicle using solid propellants exclusively. The rest of the vehicles fall into four families— Thor, Atlas, Titan, and Saturn. The Thor, Atlas, and Titan are modifications of military missiles. Saturn 1 and Uprated Saturn 1 use clusters of tanks based on the tanks of the old Redstone military missile.

Upper-stage vehicles enter into the classifications. One is the Centaur, a pioneer in burning liquid hydrogen; it flies as the Atlas-Centaur and is employed for lunar and interplanetary missions. Another upper-stage vehicle is the Agena, which is compatible with such large boosters as Thor, Atlas, and Titan 3. (Thus, in the Gemini 8 mission, an Agena ascended in an Atlas-Agena vehicle, dropped the Atlas when the Atlas had burned all its fuel, and orbited as an Agena spacecraft, or docking vehicle.)

Configurations. Not all of a vehicle's power or thrust need be applied in a single stage. Rocket engineers prefer to fashion vehicles in two or three stages—and four in the case of the Scout—to move a payload upward at ever greater velocities. The stages give the vehicle what is known as its configuration —that is, the contour, or size and shape—which is quickly indicative of its capabilities.

Thus the Gemini launch vehicle, a modified Air Force Titan 2 intercontinental ballistic missile, was said to consist of two stages, the first with two engines providing 430,000 pounds of thrust, and the second with one engine providing 100,000 pounds of thrust.

In any launch vehicle, by far the greatest power is built into the first stage, for it is at liftoff that the vehicle opposes the greatest pull of gravity—and the burden is increased because the launch vehicle is fully fueled. If the vehicle is to get off the pad, the first-stage thrust of its engine must exceed the weight of the vehicle. In the case of a Titan 2 launch vehicle and a Gemini spacecraft, the combined weight to be lifted is 340,000 pounds—and the 430,000 pound thrust of the first-stage engines more than fulfills the need. In fact, the engines create an upward force 1.26 times greater than the downward force; that is, the thrust-to-weight ratio is 1.26 to 1.

The countup, or sequence of events after liftoff, of a Gemini launch vehicle makes clear the brief but essential role that a launch vehicle plays in a mission. The countup (with "T" for "Time") reads:

T plus 2 minutes, 36 seconds: Booster (first stage) engine cuts off.

T plus 5 minutes, 41 seconds: Second-stage engine cuts off.

T plus 5 minutes, 57 seconds: Spacecraft separates from launch vehicle.

T plus 6 minutes, 7 seconds: Spacecraft inserted into orbit from 100 to 168 miles high.

In addition to the customary numbered stages (usually two or three, but sometimes four), a launch vehicle may be given a "zero stage" (or "stage zero") for use at liftoff. This stage consists of two or three solid-rocket motors that are strapped on to the sides of an existing launch vehicle, and it greatly increases the lifting capabilities of the basic vehicle without disturbing the vehicle itself.

The Atlas launch vehicle has what is known as a "half-stage," which is another—and earlier—way of supplying greater thrust at liftoff. The half-stage consists of a pair of outboard engines. When they have burned up their fuel during the ascent, the outboard engines drop off—but a single sustainer engine within the vehicle keeps on thrusting.

They're Not Missiles. The rocket became a major force in space research after Germany developed the V-2 missile to bombard Britain from Europe in World War II. Even today the military term "missile" often is applied erroneously to a rocket used as a launch vehicle in peaceful exploration.

A missile, the U.S. Air Force declares in its official glossary, is "any weapon or object designed to be thrown, dropped, projected, or self-propelled, through aerospace to a target." In contrast, "rocket" refers to a thrust-producing system. A rocket (quoting the Air Force again) "derives its thrust from ejection of hot gases generated from material carried in the system, not requiring intake of air or water." In short, the rocket engine carries its own oxygen supply—in an oxidizer —and therefore it can operate in space.

Missiles developed by the military to hurl at targets provided the power to launch U.S. spacecraft. In the early days of launch vehicles, missiles were modified only to the extent necessary to make them compatible with particular space missions. Now the Atlas standard launch vehicle typifies the newer era. Standardized guidance, autopilot, tracking, telemetry, and electrical system "kits" are provided for installation on a basic airframe. For instance, two General Electric-made guidance kits are in readiness—one for launchings from the Eastern Test Range and one from the Western Test Range. When the Titan missile was chosen to launch the manned Gemini flights, the Air Force added both a malfunction detection system to send booster performance data to the crew, and a backup flight control system.

Solid or Liquid Fuels? All rockets in the U.S. fleet of launch vehicles burn chemical fuels. Mostly the fuels are liquid, but some are solid.

A solid fuel has an advantage over some liquid fuels in

that it can be stored in the vehicle, immediately ready for use at liftoff. There are no tanks and no complicated mechanisms. However, once turned on, the solid-propellant rocket is difficult to turn off. In addition, it has a shorter burning time. (In a number of cases, solids are strapped on to a liquid-fuel core to give an extra boost on liftoff.)

A liquid fuel fires for a longer time, yields high energy, and is readily controllable. Some liquid fuels, however, cannot be stored in the launch vehicle and must be inserted shortly before liftoff.

Go-Anywhere Rockets. Questions arise about how a rocket engine differs from a jet engine. Both are internal combustion engines, burning a fuel-oxygen mixture. Both operate on the principle of action and reaction, sending hot exhaust gases rearward out a nozzle to exert thrust and send the vehicle forward. However, the jet engine "breathes" the oxygen it requires from the atmosphere, while the rocket engine contains within itself all of the oxidizer necessary for the consumption or combustion of its fuel. A jet cannot fly beyond the earth's atmosphere; a rocket can fly anywhere—and in fact its performance improves when it gets out of the atmosphere and into space.

FACTS ABOUT CURRENT U.S. LAUNCH VEHICLES

SCOUT: 72 ft. high; 3.33 ft. in diameter.
Four solid stages. *Use:* Small payloads, including Explorer satellites, high-altitude probes, and nose cone re-entry tests.

These four vehicles are based on a modified military missile, the Thor:

THOR-AGENA D: 76 ft. high; 8 ft. in diameter.
Two liquid stages. *Use:* Small payloads on Air Force and scientific missions.

THRUST-AUGMENTED THOR-AGENA D: 76 ft. high; 8 ft. in diameter.
Thor-Agena D plus three strap-on solid motors on first stage.

DELTA: 90 ft. high; 8 ft. in diameter.

    Three stages—two liquid and one solid. *Use:* TIROS and ESSA weather satellites; Syncom and other small communications satellites; scientific satellites.

THRUST-AUGMENTED DELTA: 90 ft. high; 8 ft. in diameter.

    Delta vehicle plus three solid strap-on motors on first stage. *Use:* Early Bird, Interplanetary Explorers, and others.

These two vehicles are based on a modified military missile, the Atlas D:

ATLAS-AGENA D: 104 ft. high; 10 ft. in diameter.

    Two liquid stages. *Use:* Unmanned lunar and interplanetary probes, such as Mariner, Ranger, and Lunar Orbiter; heavy earth satellites; Air Force missions.

ATLAS-CENTAUR: 113 ft. high; 10 ft. in diameter.

    Two liquid stages. *Use:* Lunar and interplanetary missions, including Surveyor.

These two vehicles are based on a modified military missile, the Titan:

TITAN 2: 90 ft. high (exc. Gemini spacecraft); 10 ft. in diameter.

    Two liquid stages: *Use:* Gemini spacecraft.

TITAN 3A: 124 ft. high; 10 ft. in diameter.

      3C: 127 ft. high; 30 ft. in diameter.

    The Titan 2 with a third liquid stage becomes the 3A; the 3A with two 120-inch solid-propellant rockets becomes the 3C.

    Use: Manned Orbiting Laboratory, earth satellites, and manned spacecraft.

These three vehicles had their beginnings in the Redstone, later modified to become the Jupiter. Each Saturn consists of clusters of tanks and engines proved in the preceding vehicle.

SATURN 1: 190 ft. high (inc. spacecraft); 21.6 ft. in diameter.

    Two liquid stages. *Use:* Unmanned Apollo program, Pegasus satellites.

UPRATED SATURN 1: 224 ft. high (inc. spacecraft); 21.6 ft. in diameter.
Two liquid stages. *Use:* Apollo spacecraft in earth orbits.

SATURN 5: 363 ft. high (inc. spacecraft); 33 ft. in diameter.
Three liquid stages. *Use:* Manned Apollo spacecraft to the moon; space stations.

launch window. The period during which a payload must be launched if it is to intercept its target. When Gemini 7 was orbiting the earth, Gemini 6 had a 47-minute launch window open—from 9:34 to 10:21 a.m.—on the day it set out in pursuit. Had that opportunity been missed, a shorter window would have been open later in the day. Interplanetary launch windows are more infrequent: for a Venus shot, a 30-day window occurs every nineteen months.

Lewis Research Center. NASA installation at Cleveland, Ohio, devoted to basic and applied research in propulsion. The 350-acre Lewis center is situated beside the Cleveland-Hopkins airport.

Lewis's scientists and engineers played major roles in managing the development of the Centaur and Agena, upper stages vital in propelling spacecraft on lunar and interplanetary missions. Lewis also explores the "way-out" powerplants of the future—nuclear and electric engines, and propulsion involving thermal and solar energy conversion processes. Space-environment chambers, rocket test-stands, and materials-testing laboratories are part of Lewis's comprehensive facilities. In addition, Lewis researchers have access to a nuclear reactor at Plum Brook Research Station, Sandusky, Ohio.

Liberty Bell 7. The Mercury spacecraft in which Virgil I. Grissom became the second American into space. On a suborbital shot on July 21, 1961, Liberty Bell 7 rose 118 miles and flew for 15 minutes, 37 seconds, in a virtual duplication of the initial flight of Alan B. Shepard, Jr.

life sciences. Research in the life sciences is directed to three main areas: (1) exobiology, the detection of life outside the earth's environment; (2) environmental biology, the interactions between man and other biological systems with the space environment; and (3) biotechnology, which has to do with the engineering support of man and the effective integration of man into the space flight system. The Life Sciences Research Laboratory at NASA's Ames Research Center, Moffett Field, Cal., is the focal point of the agency's efforts to gain new knowledge in life sciences.

life support. The sustaining and protecting of astronauts sealed in a spacecraft. The essentials include eleven pounds of water and two pounds of oxygen each day for each astronaut—a prohibitively heavy load for long space voyages unless water and air are recycled and reused.

The most advanced experimental life-support system in existence in the United States envisions the sustaining of four astronauts in space for a year, with food to be resupplied every three months. The prototype system was developed and built by General Dynamics, and was delivered in 1966 to NASA's Langley Research Center for tests. It is housed in a dome-shaped steel tank, eighteen feet high and eighteen feet in diameter, and weighs about thirty tons. The tank could be used in a manned orbiting space station.

General Dynamics designed the system for regenerating water and air indefinitely. Because food cannot yet be regenerated efficiently, dehydrated food will be stored in the capsule and resupplied. A future goal of life-support system designers is the complete "closed ecological system" in which food, too, would be regenerated.

To transform the used water into pure, fresh water, the prototype system employs an evaporative method. General Dynamics explains the procedure as follows:

"Excess vapor from the cabin air, used wash water, and urine are collected in holding tanks and are then drawn into wicks by capillary action. At the other end of the wick, water is evaporated into a stream of warmed air. The contaminants are left behind in the replaceable wicks. Condensed vapor moves through a series of filters finally to return to a central reservoir as pure water."

To make possible the reuse of air that has picked up exhaled carbon dioxide and contaminants, the life-support system continuously circulates cabin air through a bank of machinery. The equipment includes: (1) a dehumidifier, to take out excess moisture and add it to the central tanks; (2) a charcoal filter, to remove some contaminants; (3) a catalytic burner, to convert other contaminants; and (4) a separator, to remove the carbon dioxide. In another chamber, the carbon dioxide is mixed with hydrogen at a high temperature in the presence of a catalyst, creating water and pure carbon. General Dynamics explains:

"Techniques have not yet been developed to use the carbon, so it is simply blown into a storage area. But the water, collected through a porous plate, is transferred to an electrolytic cell where an electric current breaks it into hydrogen and oxygen. The hydrogen is pumped back to fuel the previous reaction in which the water was formed. The oxygen returns to the cabin air to be breathed again. "

Solid wastes are heated and dried into a powdery residue, and activated charcoal removes the odors. The wastes now are stored and may serve as shielding against radiation. For the future, scientists consider using the wastes as fuel for the propulsion system or, perhaps, to synthesize foods.

Special techniques for bathing, getting a haircut, and brushing teeth have been worked out for the experimental life-support system.

"The astronaut will have a specially saturated sponge for bathing," George Drake, General Dynamics chief of life-support engineering, said. "This sponge will be just damp enough for cleaning, but will not drip."

Plans call for each astronaut to have his head shaved bald before embarking on a space voyage. While in orbit, he would receive a trim with an electric razor or clippers, and the hair would be caught in a plastic bag so that it would not float around as a contaminating element and hazard to breathing.

The toothpaste will be edible. Instead of spitting out toothpaste, which would become a floating contaminant, the astronaut simply will swallow it.

lifting body. A wingless space vehicle that attains aerodynamic stability and lift from its body alone, so that it can be flown for long distances inside the atmosphere and maneuvered to an airplane-style touchdown at a point selected by its pilot. Glide flights of heavy (2.5-ton) lifting bodies began in 1966, to be followed by rocket-powered flights. NASA's Office of Space Technology developed two versions—the M2-F2 and HL-10—to help establish a technological base for design of future manned re-entry vehicles. The Air Force joined the testing with its SV-5. The three versions differ, but in general they look like wide, flat speedboats with high tails. The Martin Company likens the SV-5 (also known as the X-24A) to a "streamlined flatiron without the handle."

Far in the future, powered lifting-body vehicles are considered likely prospects for manned interplanetary missions. NASA also regards them as potentially valuable for spacecraft inspection, repair, and reconnaissance; search and rescue; and resupply of advanced space stations. They could also be used as an upper stage of a recoverable launch vehicle.

The lifting body's potential as a space vehicle stems from its great aerodynamic lift (high lift-drag ratio), far exceeding that of the Mercury-Gemini-Apollo series of ballistic-type spacecraft. Lift results from greater air pressure on the bottom of the body than on the top. The absence of wings eliminates many structural problems and permits a body shape that offers a large internal volume with a small surface area. Heating problems are reduced because of lower deceleration and lower temperature. The blunt shape (the Air Force speaks of its version as "an elongated teardrop") lends itself to use of ablative materials that boil away to vaporize heat.

All U.S. manned spacecraft so far have re-entered the earth's atmosphere much like a bullet and parachuted into water for recovery. Designed to use orbital energy and aerodynamic lift for in-flight maneuvering and a glide landing, the boatlike craft of the future may permit the pilot to choose a landing area possibly the size of the southern half of the United States (if the choice is made before re-entry). The lift capability would also make possible a horizontal landing on a runway.

The idea of lifting bodies was advanced in 1957 by Dr. Alfred J. Eggers, Jr. He was then an executive of NASA's Ames Research Center and later became NASA deputy associate administrator for advanced research and technology.

For details on the nation's lifting bodies, see *HL-10, M2-F2,* and *SV-5.*

liftoff. The initial motion of a space vehicle as it rises from its launching pad.

liquid hydrogen. A hard-to-tame propulsive fuel created from the normally gaseous element hydrogen by supercooling it to a liquid at minus 423° F.

Regarded as the rocket propellant of the future, liquid hydrogen—when mixed with liquid oxygen—delivers about 40 per cent more thrust per pound than the usual kerosene-type fuels. Liquid hydrogen pioneering technology is conducted in the Centaur, a high-energy upper-stage space vehicle developed by General Dynamics/Astronautics under the direction of NASA's Lewis Research Center.

Centaur requires four thermal insulation panels to minimize boiloff of the fuel. And before its two Pratt & Whitney RL-10 engines are ignited in space, they are chilled with propellants to avoid boiloff as the liquid hydrogen enters the turbopumps.

The use of liquid hydrogen is anticipated in the upper stage of most future rockets, including the Saturn 5 "moon rocket." A single ignition, as when Centaur sent the first Surveyor to the moon, has been accomplished readily. However, restarting in space has proved troublesome, apparently because of difficulty in making the fuel flow into the engines. See *fuel sloshing.*

liquid oxygen (shortened frequently to LOX). The normally gaseous element oxygen cooled so that it becomes a liquid; used as an oxidizer in rocket engines. Liquid oxygen boils at minus 297° F (this results in the white plume flowing from a point high on a rocket just before launching), and it freezes at minus 361°.

Little Joe 2. A small solid-propellant rocket used to launch Apollo spacecraft on suborbital flights from 1963 through 1966. In that span, Little Joe 2 launched four boilerplate Apollos and one production model at the White Sands Missile Range, N.M., to prove out a launch escape system as acceptable for manned Apollo missions.

Built by General Dynamics, this rocket varied in lifting capabilities from assignment to assignment because the number of motors and stages differed. In 1966, when it hurled a production spacecraft to an altitude of about 70,000 feet, Little Joe delivered 579,775 pounds of thrust—from four Aerojet-General Algol motors (103,200 pounds of thrust each) and five Thiokol Recruit motors (33,395 pounds of thrust each). Two Algols and five Recruits were ignited on the ground as the first stage; two more Algols were started as the second stage thirty-seven seconds after liftoff.

LOX. See *liquid oxygen.*

Luna (formerly translated Lunik). Soviet spacecraft aimed at the moon.

On Jan. 2, 1959, Luna 1 became the first payload to escape toward the moon. It missed the moon and went into sun orbit. On Sept. 13 that year, Luna 2 smashed into the moon, and on Oct. 7 Luna 3 photographed the far side of the moon from 4,373 miles, later transmitting the photos.

On Feb. 3, 1966, Luna 9 became the first object to land softly on the moon and send back photographs from the surface. The 1.5-ton vehicle did a half-gainer in space and turned on its retrorocket forty-eight seconds before landing. In addition, a shock-absorbing device was used. Just before impact, a smaller sphere—weighing 220 pounds and twice as big as a basketball—was thrown clear. Later this sphere opened, much like a flower, to free its picture-taking equipment.

Launched on Mar. 31, 1966, Luna 10 became the first moon-orbiting satellite. The picture-taking Luna 11, launched Aug. 24, 1966, became a moon-orbiting satellite and made 277 circuits before ceasing transmission on Oct. 1, 1966. Luna 12, launched Oct. 12, 1966, sent back photos of the moon's surface. Luna 13 landed softly on the moon's Ocean of Storms on Dec. 24, 1966, and took 12-inch-deep soil samples which indicated that the moon's soil is of medium density and similar to that on earth.

lunar module. A 16-ton "moon bug" or space ferry, designed to take two astronauts from the Apollo spacecraft to the surface of the moon and back to the spacecraft. The lunar module (originally called a lunar excursion module or LEM) is the third module of the Apollo spacecraft. The module is a four-legged device looking much like Surveyor 1. Grumman Aircraft Engineering Corp. is the prime contractor. The craft has two engines of its own—a TRW Systems lunar descent engine for a soft landing, and a Bell Aerosystems ascent engine for the climb back up to the Apollo's parking orbit.

Lunar Module 1 (LM-1) was boosted into space Jan. 22, 1968, for an unmanned test in earth orbit (the Apollo 5 mission). The LM-1 was launched from Complex 37 at Cape Kennedy by an Uprated Saturn 1 rocket (AS-204). The ascent propulsion system (in the upper half of the spacecraft) and the descent propulsion system (in the lower half, which serves as a launching platform on the moon) were fired in flight and demonstrated their abilities to perform successfully.

Lunar Orbiter. A U.S. flying photographic laboratory designed to circle the moon, take photographs of possible sites for manned landings, and radio them to earth. The Orbiter is a truncated cone from which four solar-cell panels project. When the panels are folded back for launch, the 850-pound spacecraft measures only 5.5 x 5 feet. Two cameras and a full photo lab are carried inside an egg-shaped pressure shell.

The Boeing Company builds Orbiter for NASA. Eastman Kodak Company (camera system) and Radio Corporation of America (power and communications systems) are the main subcontractors.

Lunar Orbiter 1 reached the moon on Aug. 14, 1966, after a 92-hour flight. At a point about 550 miles from the moon, the craft fired a retrorocket that slowed it down, permitting it to be captured by the moon's gravitational field. As a satellite of the moon, Lunar Orbiter 1 made a counterclockwise orbit about every 3.5 hours. Its perilune, or closest point to the moon, was 117 miles.

Lunar Orbiter 2, launched Nov. 6, 1966, obtained more spectacular pictures than its predecessor did. Highlights included the first photos—from 28 miles away—of the Crater of Copernicus, one of the main features on the face of the moon.

In 1967 the three launchings were completed about three months apart—Orbiter 3 on Feb. 4, Orbiter 4 on May 4, and Orbiter 5 on Aug. 1. Among Orbiter 3's accomplishments was the photographing of Surveyor 1 sitting on the moon's

NASA

The first view of the earth taken by a spacecraft (Lunar Orbiter 1) from the vicinity of the moon.

surface. Orbiter 4 obtained telephoto pictures of 99 percent of the moon's face with ten times finer resolution than the best telescope views from earth, and it also added to photo coverage of the hidden side of the moon. Orbiter 5, besides obtaining low-altitude lunar-site pictures, snapped the nearly full face of earth from lunar orbit. The Lunar Orbiter project ended on Jan. 31, 1968, when NASA controllers signaled Orbiter 5 to crash into the face of the moon.

An Atlas-Agena launch vehicle boosted each Orbiter from

Cape Kennedy. The upper-stage Agena, firing a second time from a parking orbit, started the Orbiter toward the moon—at 24,400 mph—through a narrow translunar injection point 119 miles above the earth.

LUT (for launch umbilical tower). See *mobile launcher*.

M2-F2 (M for "manned" and F2 for the second modification of the shape). A wingless lifting body with a flat top, rounded bottom, and half-conical design. There are two vertical fins at the rear. The M2-F2 is under study for possible future use as a returnable, reusable spacecraft.

Length: 22 ft., 2 in.
Width: 9 ft., 7 in.
Height: 8 ft., 10 in. (to top of fins)
Weight: 5,000 lbs.

The M2-F2 made its first manned glide flight on July 12, 1966, when it was dropped from a B-52 flying at 45,000 feet, glided for four minutes and landed at Edwards Air Force Base at about 200 mph. It was piloted by Milton O. Thompson, NASA's chief project pilot on the lifting body program at the NASA Flight Research Center, Edwards, Cal.

Bruce A. Peterson, NASA research pilot, was severely injured and the M2-F2 was extensively damaged in a crash while landing on May 10, 1967, in its sixteenth glide flight.

The Northrop Corp. builds the M2-F2 for NASA's Ames Research Center. See *lifting body*.

magnetometer. The basic device for measuring magnetic fields. Magnetometers thus become an essential payload on spacecraft that make magnetic field experiments, such as Interplanetary Explorers operating between the earth and the moon. An additional requirement for these spacecraft is that all parts, and the fully assembled craft as well, be handled under the strictest "clean room" conditions during production to keep them magnetically clean.

magnetosphere. "That part of the earth's atmosphere which exists by virtue of the earth's magnetic field. The magnetosphere consists of trapped particles, mainly electrons and protons, which spiral about the magnetic lines of force from pole to pole, and gradually precess eastward or westward, depending on their charge. Particles are lost by the magnetosphere when they descend into the atmosphere at high latitudes. It is believed that particles are fed into the magnetosphere by effects associated with the arrival of plasma clouds ejected during solar flares as well as from the beta decay of neutrons produced by cosmic rays striking the upper atmosphere. Particles may also be injected into the magnetosphere by high-altitude nuclear explosions."—(American Institute of Physics) See *atmosphere*.

"majority-rule" circuit. To assure reliability, each circuit is triplicated in critical sections of the computer that will steer and in the Saturn 5 launch vehicle and its Apollo spacecraft. Triple redundancy allows for the possibility that an electronic part might fail and issue an incorrect signal. If so, the computer will disregard it and pass on only the correct signals from the other two portions of the circuit. Thus International Business Machines Corp. has built what is called a "2-out-of-3-vote" or "majority-rule" circuit. See also *redundant*.

maneuver controller. The device—in effect, a stick—used by a command pilot to thrust his Gemini spacecraft in any of three directions in a rendezvous, docking, or other maneuver while in earth orbit. The spacecraft may move forward or aft, up or down, left or right. An on-board guidance computer measures each movement and puts the pilot on a collision course with his target.

Manned Orbiting Laboratory (MOL). An earth-orbiting space station being developed by the Air Force and considered to be one of the most important new government research programs since Apollo. An MOL consists of a new Gemini spacecraft (the Gemini-B) and an attached cylindrical laboratory ten feet in diameter and forty feet long. Two crewmen are to leave the spacecraft through a hatch in the shield and enter the laboratory to work for thirty days in a "shirt-sleeve environment" (unhampered by pressure suits).

The Air Force named Douglas Aircraft's Missile and Space Systems Division as prime contractor in 1965. A Martin-built Titan 3-C rocket will be assigned to put MOL into a polar orbit ranging from 100 to 150 miles above the earth.

MOL's purpose was defined by Secretary of the Air Force Eugene M. Zuckert, testifying before a Congressional committee in 1964: "The Manned Orbiting Laboratory program is a research program aimed at giving man the opportunity to operate in space so that we may determine whether and when the manned space vehicle will be militarily significant. The MOL program will provide much of the supporting knowledge of indicated future manned space missions. . . . Our primary need is to know what functions man can perform in orbit."

In addition, it is generally recognized that an MOL could serve both as an orbiting command post and as a reconnaissance vehicle because in a polar orbit it will fly over every part of the earth once daily.

manned space flight (United States). Three manned spaceflight projects, each requiring years for completion, have been advancing the competence of the United States in space exploration.

The increased size of the spacecraft with each successive project indicates how missions steadily become more ambitious and more complex. The progression as the National Aeronautics and Space Administration has improved its basic knowledge of space flight has been:

Project Mercury—one-man spacecraft (2,700 lbs.)

Project Gemini—two-man spacecraft (7,000 lbs.)

Project Apollo—three-man spacecraft (95,000 lbs.)

Each manned spacecraft contains a pressurized crew compartment—called a cabin in Mercury and Gemini and a command module in Apollo. The crew compartment supplies the astronauts with an environment much like that in which man lives on earth. Controls provide oxygen for breathing and ventilation. They also regulate barometric pressure and humidity and remove unpleasant odors and toxic materials. Titanium and magnesium construction protects the astronauts inside the Mercury and Gemini spacecraft; brazed honeycomb steel, covered with a special material that boils to a gas (ablates) at high temperatures, shields Apollo crews from the space environment.

A summary of U.S. manned space flights:

Mission	Spacecraft Time (Hrs. Min. Sec.)	Revolutions
MR-3: Shepard	0:15:22	—
MR-4: Grissom	0:15:37	—
MA-6: Glenn	4:55:23	3
MA-7: Carpenter	4:56:05	3
MA-8: Schirra	9:13:11	6
MA-9: Cooper	34:19:49	22
Gemini 3: Grissom, Young	4:53:00	3
Gemini 4: McDivitt, White	97:56:11	62
Gemini 5: Cooper, Conrad	190:56:01	120
Gemini 7: Borman, Lovell	330:35:13	206
Gemini 6: Schirra, Stafford	25:51:24	15
Gemini 8: Armstrong, Scott	10:42:06	6.6
Gemini 9: Stafford, Cernan	72:20:56	44
Gemini 10: Young, Collins	70:46:45	43
Gemini 11: Conrad, Gordon	71:17:08	44
Gemini 12: Lovell, Aldrin	94:34:30	59

Total manned time in Project Mercury and Gemini is 1,993 hours, 41 minutes, 55 seconds. For dates and details of those flights, see *Gemini* and *Mercury*.

In the Apollo project, the disaster that had been feared in earlier manned activity occurred—but it came unexpectedly in a ground test. Three astronauts—Virgil I. Grissom, Edward H. White II, and Roger Chaffee—died in a flash fire in the Apollo 204 spacecraft as it sat atop an unfueled rocket at Launch Complex 34, Cape Kennedy, at 6:31 pm on Jan. 27, 1967. The Apollo 204 mission was to have been launched on Feb. 21, 1967. Further manned flights were held off, however, for an intensive safety study, redesign of the hatch for quick escape, and removal of nearly all combustible material from Apollo spacecraft. See *Apollo*.

manned space flight (USSR). The USSR sent the first two astronauts in space in 1961, and widened its lead over American efforts in 1964 by launching the first three-man crew. In 1966, however, the USSR did not launch a manned flight while the U.S. was carrying out five manned missions.

A summary of the USSR's manned space flights:

Vostok (meaning "east")—(Apr. 12, 1961). Maj. Yuri A. Gagarin completed one orbit in about 89 minutes. This milestone flight demonstrated that man can survive in space.

Vostok 2 (Aug. 6–7, 1961). Maj. Gherman S. Titov completed seventeen orbits in 25 hours, 11 minutes. This flight demonstrated that man can eat and sleep in a weightless state.

Vostok 3 (launched Aug. 11, 1962). Piloted by Maj. Andrian G. Nikolayev; flew sixty-four orbits in 94 hours, 25 minutes.

Vostok 4 (launched Aug. 12, 1962). Piloted by Lt. Col. Pavel R. Popovich; flew forty-eight orbits in 70 hours, 59 minutes. Passed within four miles of Vostok 3.

Vostok 5 (launched June 14, 1963). Piloted by Lt. Col. Valeri F. Bykovski; in orbit for 4 days, 23 hours, 6 minutes.

Vostok 6 (launched June 16, 1963). Piloted by Valentina V. Tereshkova, first woman astronaut; flew 2 days, 22 hours, 50 minutes. Passed within three miles of Vostok 5.

Voshod (meaning "sunrise")—(Oct. 12–13, 1964). With Col. Vladimir M. Komarov, pilot-cosmonaut; Dr. Boris B. Yegorov, physician; and Konstantin P. Feoktistov, engineer and spacecraft designer; completed sixteen orbits in 24 hours, 17 minutes. This was the first multi-manned space flight. It marked the entry into space of a working team of specialists from various branches of science and technology. All three occupants wore lightweight woolen suits rather than spacesuits. Postflight reports conceded that all three showed the effects of weightlessness.

Voskhod 2 (Mar. 18–19, 1965). Col. Pavel Belyayev and Aleksei Leonov completed seventeen orbits in 1 day, 2 hours, 2 minutes. Leonov, wearing a spacesuit, left the spacecraft through a submarine-type airlock, took history's first space walk for ten minutes and returned.

Soyuz 1 (April 23-24, 1967): Cosmonaut Vladimir A. Komarov was killed when the parachute fouled during the re-entry of this new spacecraft into the atmosphere, causing it to plummet to earth. There were indications that frequent troubles plagued his eighteen-orbit space flight.

The Vostok, at an estimated weight of 10,000 pounds, was heavier than the U.S. first-generation Mercury spacecraft

(2,900 pounds). The Voskhod, at an estimated 11,500 pounds, was heavier than the second-generation Gemini spacecraft (7,000 pounds). Americans believe that a thrust of about 900,000 pounds was required to place the Voskhods in earth orbit. (This compares with 530,000 pounds of thrust for the Gemini standard launch vehicle and a first-stage thrust of 7,500,000 pounds for the Saturn 5 launch vehicle used in Project Apollo). The Soyuz, intended for use as the command unit of a larger spacecraft, is estimated to weigh 15,000 pounds.

Manned Space Flight Network (MSFN). A network of NASA and Department of Defense facilities used for information and control of manned missions. Flight controllers are provided continuous tracking, command, and telemetry data. The Real-Time Computer Complex at Houston's Manned Spacecraft Center supplies computing support.

The tracking network: Cape Kennedy, Merritt Island, and Patrick Air Force Base, all near the launch site; Grand Bahama Island; Ascension Island; Antigua Island; Bermuda; Pretoria, South Africa; Kano, Nigeria; Carnarvon, Australia; Grand Canary Island; Point Arguello, Cal.; White Sands, N.M.; Kauai, Hawaii; U.S. Navy Ships *Rose Knot, Coastal Sentry,* and *Range Tracker;* Canton Island; Grand Turk Island; Tananarive, Malagasy; Eglin, Fla.; and Corpus Christi, Tex.

Manned Spacecraft Center (MSC). NASA installation near Houston, Tex., responsible for managing the development and operation of manned spacecraft. MSC's responsibilities extend all the way from training astronauts to controlling space flights from launch to impact.

The public is best acquainted with the Houston center through observation of its Mission Control Center on television during manned flights. Houston also serves as the computer center for manned flights, and its Real-Time Computer Complex (RTCC) immediately analyzes information as it arrives from the Manned Space Flight Tracking Network.

MSC sectors include operations, administration, research and development, and engineering. In all, MSC covers 1,620 acres.

Mariner. NASA's designation for a series of unmanned spacecraft that make scientific exploration journeys to the vicinity of the nearest planets—Venus, closer to the sun, and thus with an orbit inside that of the earth; and Mars, farther from the sun, and thus with an orbit outside that of the earth.

Mariner 2. A history-making spacecraft that gave man his first look at another planet, Venus, from a comparatively close distance (21,648 miles) and contributed considerable early (1962) information about interplanetary space. Built by NASA's Jet Propulsion Laboratory, Mariner 2 was launched on Aug. 27, 1962, by an Atlas-Agena B vehicle and reached the vicinity of Venus on Dec. 14 of that year. On the way, the 449-pound Mariner 2 developed evidence that the solar wind (hot gases) rushes outward steadily from the sun. After its Dec. 14 flyby of the planet, Mariner 2 kept in contact up to 53.9 million miles from the earth. On Jan. 3, 1963, communications ceased. See *Venus.*

Mariner 4. After 325 million miles of space travel in a wide-swinging path, Mariner 4 gave the world its first close inspection of the planet Mars on July 14, 1965. In what is termed an "encounter," the spacecraft moved to within 6,118 miles of the planet. Focusing a TV camera, it took twenty-one dramatic pictures to provide much new scientific information.

This JPL-built craft weighed 575 pounds. It was octagonally shaped, measuring 50 inches across, and had a 22½-foot wingspread consisting of solar panels to generate electric power for spacecraft circuits. It was launched Nov. 28, 1964, by an Atlas-Agena vehicle, and required 228 days to reach the vicinity of Mars. So accurate and reliable were the launch vehicle, midcourse motor, attitude controls, and other components that the "miss" from the aiming point was only about 1,000 miles in a 325-million mile flight. After the flyby, Mariner 4 entered a perpetual orbit around the sun. On Oct. 1, 1965, communications were shut off, after the spacecraft had returned 13 million engineering measurements and 23 million scientific measurements.

In 1966, with the advent of the Goldstone 210-foot-diameter antenna, Mariner 4 was contacted again over a 197.5-million-mile radio link. On the second anniversary of its launch, the craft had operated continuously in space for more than 17,000 hours—almost 300 per cent of its design life of 6,000 hours. In its first two years, Mariner 4 flew 1,025,082,830 miles.

Mariner 5. This 540-pound spacecraft passed within 2,554 miles of Venus on Oct. 19, 1967, and carried out specially designed experiments to probe the planet's atmosphere. Mariner 5 reported no layers of radiation such as the earth's Van Allen belts.

Mariner 5 was launched from Cape Kennedy on June 14, 1967, by an Atlas-Agena D vehicle. It had been built as a "backup" for Mariner 4—a Mars mission—but it was later modified for a flight toward the sun rather than away from it. (Solar panels, for instance, were reduced in size.) To reach the vicinity of Venus, Mariner 5 flew 217 million miles in a wide arc.

Mariner Mars '69 Spacecraft. A heavier and more sophisticated spacecraft based on the technology of previous Mariners. In 1965 preparations began for launching two of these spacecraft in 1969 on nine-month missions to Mars. (Opportunities to launch vehicles toward Mars come only once every twenty-five months.) Each craft will weigh 800 pounds and will be launched by an Atlas-Centaur from Cape Kennedy.

Tentative plans call for the Mariners to fly by the planet at an altitude of about 2,000 miles. Scientific equipment aboard will include two TV cameras, ultraviolet and infrared spectrometers, an infrared radiometer, an S-band occultation experiment, and a celestial mechanics experiment. The occultation experiment involves changes in the tracking and telemetry signal as the spacecraft passes behind Mars, and will provide information on the composition, density, and extent of the Martian atmosphere. The celestial mechanics investigation involves an analysis of tracking data to improve knowledge of the precise orbits of Mars and the earth, and other information.

Mars (planet). The fourth planet of the solar system, in order of distance from the sun, after Mercury, Venus, and Earth. At its closest point, reached once every fifteen years, Mars comes within about 35 million miles of the earth. Mars— known as the "red planet" for its brick color—requires 687 earth days to make one revolution about the sun. A launch window, or favorable opportunity for sending a spacecraft from earth to Mars as both planets wheel about the sun in separate orbits, occurs every twenty-five months.

Mars is only 4,212 to 4,218 miles in diameter, in contrast to the earth, which has a diameter of 7,927 miles. It has an extremely thin atmosphere, nearly comparable to the earth's atmosphere at an altitude of twenty miles, and consisting mostly of carbon dioxide, as well as some nitrogen and argon. Mars has two moons—Phobos and Deimos.

Spectacular new knowledge about Mars was contributed by NASA's Mariner 4 as it swept by the planet at a distance of 6,118 miles on July 14, 1965. Mariner's cameras brought the planet thirty times closer than any telescope had done, and revealed surprisingly that the surface of Mars is covered with meteoroid craters much like those on the moon. There was no evidence of "canals," water, or life. Consequently Mars was regarded as much more like the moon than like the earth—a reversal of earlier belief. Mariner's instruments revealed no measurable dust belt, magnetic field, or radiation belt. Temperatures appeared to range from 85° F at the equator to 40 below zero at the north pole. Additional close-up information will be sought with more Mariner probes.

Mars 1. A one-ton unmanned probe that the USSR launched toward Mars on Nov. 1, 1962. Mars 1 is believed to have passed the planet as planned, but the flight failed to yield any scientific results because radio contact was lost on Mar. 21, 1964, at 66 million miles into the flight.

Marshall Space Flight Center. NASA installation that manages development of launch vehicles, notably the Saturn "moon rocket." The center is named for General George C. Marshall and is situated at Redstone Arsenal, ten miles from Huntsville, Ala.

Gigantic test stands for static firings dominate a landscape that includes facilities for engineering, fabrication, testing, and laboratory work. Marshall supervises industrial contracts involving hundreds of millions of dollars yearly. Although Marshall has an extensive manufacturing capability of its own, Dr. Wernher von Braun, director, said that it is "Marshall policy to transfer research and development work, as well as fabrication, from 'in house' to contractor plants as soon as practical."

Marshall's "Huntsville Team" of scientists and engineers was responsible for placing Explorer 1 in orbit as the nation's first satellite and also developed the Mercury-Redstone rocket that launched the first two American astronauts.

Marshall Space Flight Center also directs:

Michoud Assembly Facility—A 45-acre plant for manufacturing Saturn booster stages in suburban New Orleans. This plant produced PT boats in World War II and Chrysler-built tank engines in the Korean War. It was idle from 1953 until 1961, when NASA selected it for space programs.

Mississippi Test Facility—A 142,000-acre site in southeast Mississippi with test stands for static firing. After rockets pass their tests at this proving ground, they are sent by barge to the John F. Kennedy Space Center for final assembly and launching.

maser (acronym for microwave amplification by stimulated emission of radiation). A device to produce or amplify electromagnetic waves. In space communications, a maser is used in steerable antennas to amplify signals from spacecraft. Thus, in the Goldstone "210" antenna, a maser amplifies a signal before it is contaminated by electronic noise from the receiver system. Because heat causes noises, the Goldstone maser is kept at minus 452° F by immersion in liquid helium.

mass. The total amount of matter in a body, and thus its inertia. In contrast, weight is the measure of the earth's gravitational pull on a body. Mass and weight are equal at the earth's surface. In space, mass remains constant while weight drops to zero.

mass ratio. "The ratio of the mass of the propellant charge of a rocket to the total mass of the rocket charged with the propellant."—(NASA)

Mechta (Russian for "dream"). The USSR's name for Luna 1, which was the first vehicle to escape earth's gravity. Launched on Jan. 2, 1959, Mechta passed the moon and went into orbit around the sun.

memory. A computer part that stores and then gives information to a computer which, in rockets and spacecraft, provides guidance. For use in space, International Business Machines Corp. has developed a 2.5-pound memory about the size of a baseball. Its only moving part is a hollow one-and-seven-eighths-inch cylinder on which guidance data are stored magnetically. The memory is capable of spinning up to twelve thousand revolutions per minute.

Orbiting Astronomical Observatory 1 provides an example of the use of an on-board memory system. Its memory stored 128 commands, for experiments and control, and they were executed automatically when the scientific spacecraft was out of range of the three ground stations serving it.

Mercury (planet). The planet nearest the sun. At a distance of 36 million miles, Mercury revolves about the sun in eighty-eight days. With a diameter of 3,100 miles, it is the smallest of the planets. Space explorers are more interested in Venus, which lies between Mercury and the earth.

Mercury (project). Project Mercury rocketed the first six United States astronauts into space, one by one.

The project proved, in its six manned flights, the ability of man to survive the high-gravity forces of launching, to control a craft in space, to eat and sleep while in a weightless state, and to survive a fiery re-entry plunge through the atmosphere. The McDonnell Aircraft Company, builder of the Mercury spacecraft, summed up Project Mercury as providing "the design base and experience for space operations in earth orbit."

NASA supplied leadership for the project, and selected McDonnell on Jan. 12, 1959, to build the Mercury spacecraft. An unmanned flight on July 29, 1960, opened the series, and L. Gordon Cooper's splashdown on May 16, 1963, closed it. Key members of the Mercury team included the armed forces; Chrysler, which with its subcontractors built the Redstone launch vehicle; General Dynamics, which with its contractors built the Atlas launch vehicle; and Western Electric and other firms that assisted with the worldwide communications and tracking network. McDonnell had four thousand subcontractors and suppliers.

Before sending its first two astronauts into suborbital flight, NASA first dispatched a chimpanzee, Ham, on a suborbital flight. And before putting its first astronaut into orbit, NASA first placed another chimpanzee, Enos, into orbit. (Earlier, in 1959, the monkeys Able and Baker had been rocketed into suborbital flight by a Jupiter missile. These simian journeys led to the comment that, in the evolution of space exploration, monkeys ascended before man.)

The record of the Mercury missions that carried no astronauts:

Mercury-Atlas 1 (July 29, 1960). A test that proved the ability of a Mercury spacecraft to withstand the heat of re-entry into the earth's atmosphere.

Mercury-Redstone 1A (Dec. 19, 1960). Successful test flight to an altitude of 135 miles. (The first mission in the Mercury-Redstone series was postponed on Nov. 21, 1960, when the engine cut off before liftoff.)

Mercury-Redstone 2 (Jan. 31, 1961). Astro-chimp Ham flew 155 miles high and 420 miles downrange, and was recovered from the Atlantic.

Mercury-Atlas 2 (Feb. 21, 1961). Attained an altitude of 108 miles and traveled a distance of 1,425 miles.

Mercury-Atlas 3 (Apr. 25, 1961). The launch vehicle was destroyed by radio command forty seconds after launching, but the spacecraft was recovered and used in the Mercury-Atlas 4 mission.

Mercury-Atlas 4 (Sept. 13, 1961). A Mercury spacecraft was placed in orbit for the first time; it circled the earth once. It carried a "mechanical man" that "breathed" oxygen at the same rate as a man.

Mercury-Atlas 5 (Nov. 29, 1961). As a prelude to John Glenn's flight, astro-chimp Ham orbited the earth twice and was recovered from the ocean.

The six manned flights, of course, drew tremendously greater interest. While the world watched tensely, American astronauts accomplished the following missions in space:

Mercury-Redstone 3 (May 5, 1961). Comdr. Alan B. Shepard, Jr., Navy, in Freedom 7, made a suborbital flight about 116 miles high and a distance of 302 miles down the Atlantic range from Cape Canaveral. Flight time: 15 minutes, 22 seconds.

Mercury-Redstone 4 (July 21, 1961). Capt. Virgil I. Grissom, Air Force, in Liberty Bell 7, made a suborbital flight 118 miles high and a distance of 303 miles. Flight time: 15 minutes, 37 seconds.

Mercury-Atlas 6 (Feb. 20, 1962). Col. John H. Glenn, Jr., Marine Corps, in Friendship 7, completed three orbits in 4 hours, 55 minutes, 23 seconds.

Mercury-Atlas 7 (May 24, 1962). Lt. Comdr. M. Scott Carpenter, Navy, in Aurora 7, completed three orbits in 4 hours, 56 minutes, 5 seconds.

Mercury-Atlas 8 (Oct. 3, 1962). Comdr. Walter M. Schirra, Jr., Navy, in Sigma 7, completed six orbits in 9 hours, 13 minutes, 11 seconds.

Mercury-Atlas 9 (May 15–16, 1963). Maj. L. Gordon Cooper, Jr., Air Force, in Faith 7, completed twenty-two orbits in 34 hours, 19 minutes, 49 seconds.

mesosphere. "A region of decreasing temperature immediately above the stratosphere, extending roughly from an altitude of 60 to 90 kilometers [about 37 to 56 miles]."—(American Institute of Physics)

meteoroid. A small solid body moving through space, of a size much smaller than an asteroid (a minor planet) but considerably larger than an atom or molecule. Upon entering the earth's atmosphere, a meteoroid becomes a meteorite and usually burns up (as a "shooting star"). A fragment that reaches the surface of the earth without burning up completely is called a meteorite.

The thousands of meteoroids moving through space present dangers to spacecraft and their crews, the greatest of which are punctures of pressurized cabins or of tanks containing propellants. The first extensive measurements of meteoroid hazards were obtained by three big-winged Pegasus satellites, which in a year of travel near earth recorded 1,100 punctures. NASA reported that Pegasus findings "confirmed that Apollo manned lunar landing spacecraft will be adequately protected against meteoroids." However, when larger spacecraft make longer journeys in the future, NASA foresees "design problems in protecting against probable meteoroid penetrations."

meteorology. The science that deals with the atmosphere and its phenomena, including wind, temperature, and air density. In their role as weather forecasters, meteorologists were aided in the 1960's by the introduction of weather-observation satellites—regarded as among the most significant advances in meteorology in the twentieth century. Each year, hundreds of storm bulletins are issued on the basis of observations made by cameras in the sky. For details of weather satellites, see *Environmental Science Services Administration, Nimbus,* and *Television and Infrared Observation Satellite.*

minor planet. See *asteroid.*

mission. For a spacecraft, a task or an objective. Thus: "A Surveyor mission designed to achieve a soft landing on the moon" or "a Mars mission by Mariner 4."

mobile launcher. A combination of platform and 380-foot-tall umbilical tower used to handle the Apollo/Saturn 5 vehicle at Complex 39, Kennedy Space Center. Originally it was called a launch umbilical tower. The Apollo/Saturn 5 vehicle is assembled on a mobile launcher in the shelter of the Vertical Assembly Building. Then both the vehicle and the mobile launcher are moved together 3.1 miles on a giant crawler, or transporter, to Pad A or Pad B. Nine arms extend from the tower to carry electrical, pneumatic, and propellant lines to the space vehicle. Complex 39 has three mobile launchers.

MOL. See *Manned Orbiting Laboratory.*

Molniya (meaning "lightning"). The USSR's series of communications satellites. The first two Molniya satellites were placed in long, looping orbits (about 300 by 2,500 miles) in 1965. The first of them won international attention with word that it transmitted color television programs between Moscow and Vladivostok.

By late 1967 seven Molniya satellites were aloft. The Soviet news agency Tass said that they were to serve a television network of twenty or more earth stations, as well as to handle long-distance telephone and telegraph radio communications within the USSR.

moon. The natural satellite of the earth, sometimes as near as 220,700 miles and never more than 246,900 miles away. Its mean distance from earth is about 233,000 miles.

As a target for spacecraft and an area for exploration, the moon is much smaller than the earth—it has a diameter of 2,160 miles, in contrast to 7,927 miles for earth.

For landings, the moon offers little help in braking a spacecraft from high speed to a slow descent because of its thin atmosphere—only about 4 to 10 millibars as against 1,000 millibars for earth at sea level. The moon has many peaks of 20,000-foot height and about 30,000 craters on the side visible to earth. However, there are level but pebbly plains, and with the safe descent of the 2,194-pound Surveyor 1 on a plain it became apparent that the surface will support a spacecraft.

NASA

In this photograph, taken by Lunar Orbiter 2, the floor of Copernicus is shown.

For living conditions, the moon is consistently inhospitable —the temperature reaches an estimated 214° F when the sun is at its zenith in two-week-long daylight, and plunges to about minus 250° F in two weeks of night.

The moon was first hit by a spacecraft—the USSR's Luna 2 —on Sept. 13, 1959. But it was not until Feb. 3, 1966, that close-up lunar research by spacecraft got started; on that date Luna 9 was brought to a landing soft enough to permit it to radio photographs of the moon's surface back to earth. The USSR's Luna 10 (April, 1966) and Luna 11 (August, 1966) orbited the moon to gather data on radiation and other factors vital to a manned landing. The United States began its close-up lunar research on June 1, 1966, with Surveyor 1, which landed softly and took about 11,000 excellent photos of the surface. In August, 1966, the U.S. Lunar Orbiter 1 obtained the first picture of the earth from the area of the moon; two months later, Lunar Orbiter 2 took spectacular photos of the surface from as close as twenty-eight miles. The USSR's Luna 12 took that nation's first close-up photos from orbit in October, 1966.

Surveyor 3 added to knowledge about the moon's soil when, in April 1967, it dug a mechanical claw into the surface and photographed the activity. The claw left a clear impression, and indications were that the moon's surface— at least at the point where digging occurred—was much like common volcanic rock on earth.

moon surface experiments. Seven scientific experiments have been chosen by NASA to be placed on the moon's surface by astronauts. The experiments will be housed in 150-pound packages and will be carried in the lunar module that will descend from an Apollo spacecraft to the surface of the moon. When activated on the surface, each package—an Apollo Lunar Surface Experiments Package, or ALSEP—will transmit information to earth for from six months to one year. Some packages may contain more than one experiment.

Active Lunar Seismic Experiment. This experiment seeks facts on physical properties of the moon to a depth of five hundred feet. An instrument will record the tremors as an astronaut strikes the surface with a thumping device. It also will register the tremors when small projectiles land after being fired from a mortar.

Passive Lunar Seismic Experiment. A three-axis seismometer will seek to learn whether the moon has a crust and core, and whether it consists of layers. The instrument measures lunar tremors or moon quakes.

Heat Flow Measurements. This experiment will provide data on the thermal history of the moon by measuring the flow of heat from the interior through the surface. It also will measure the distribution of radioactive elements.

Lunar Tri-Axis Magnetometer. The moon's integral magnetic field will be measured by this instrument.

Medium-Energy Solar Wind Experiment. A plasma spectrometer will determine the direction and velocity of electrons, protons, and alpha particles in the solar wind as they arrive at the moon. The instrument also will measure the effect of the particles and the moon's surface on each other.

Low-Energy Solar Wind Experiment. This study concerns particles in low-energy ranges.

Suprathermal Ion Detector. Ions will be sampled in a wide range of energies. The objective is to learn how strongly the solar wind affects the moon's ionosphere.

MSC. See *Manned Spacecraft Center.*

NASA. See *National Aeronautics and Space Administration.*

NASCOM (for *NASA Com*munications Network). A worldwide ground communications network that supplies teletype, data, and voice links between ground stations and control centers. In the Gemini manned flights, it linked eighty-nine stations, including thirty-four overseas points. The Goddard Space Flight Center, Greenbelt, Md., is responsible for NASCOM.

National Aeronautics and Space Administration (NASA). Civilian agency of the United States government that directs the nation's program for peaceful exploration of space "for the benefit of all mankind."

NASA dates from 1958, when Congress assigned it responsibility for aeronautical and space activities aside from those of a military nature. The organization began operating Oct. 1, 1958, with the staff and physical facilities of the National Advisory Committee for Aeronautics.

Challenged by an assignment even larger and costlier than developing the atomic bomb, NASA enlisted scientists, engineers, administrators, and technicians in its own employ. In addition, the total manpower devoted to the space program increased manyfold by the awarding of contracts to private industry, universities, and research institutions. Under agreements, the Department of Defense participated in many phases of the program.

Physical facilities and equipment of NASA include specialized space flight and research centers across the nation, and a network of tracking and data acquisition centers around the world.

NASA headquarters, situated in downtown Washington,

D.C., directs its organiz‌
tures known as "offices."

NAS‌
Washin‌
Office of M
George C. Marshall Spac‌
Manned Spacecraft Cente‌
John F. Kennedy Space C‌
Office of Space
Goddard Space Flight Cei‌
Jet Propulsion Laborator‌
  contract by California I‌
Wallops Station, Wallops‌
Office of Advance
Ames Research Center, Moffett Field, Cal.
Flight Research Center, Edwards, Cal.
Langley Research Center, Hampton, Va.
Lewis Research Center, Cleveland, Ohio
Electronics Research Center, Cambridge, Mass.
Office of Tracking and Data Acquisition
Washington, D.C. 20546 (NASA Headquarters)

NERVA

126

It cannot be seen with‌
31,000 miles in dia‌
believed to be ex‌
NERVA. See N‌
Nimbus. NA‌
weather‌
satelli‌

National Range Division (NRD). A division created within the Air Force Systems Command (AFSC) in 1964. The NRD includes the Air Force Eastern Test Range at Patrick Air Force Base, Fla., and the Air Force Western Test Range at Vandenberg Air Force Base, Cal.

The NRD's commanding general, whose headquarters are at Andrews Air Force Base, Washington, D.C., functions also as the AFSC deputy commander for global range. The NRD plans, develops, operates, maintains, and controls range and flight-test facilities to support national space and ballistic missile programs.

Navigation Satellite. See *Transit,* the name originally given this satellite.

NDS. See *Nuclear Detection Satellites.*

Neptune. A planet so distant from the sun that it requires 164.8 years to make a circuit. Neptune is the eighth planet from the sun, with a mean distance of almost 2.8 billion miles.

the naked eye. It is about 28,000 to
␣eter and has two satellites. Its surface is
␣eedingly cold, possibly minus 300° F.

␣uclear Engine for Rocket Vehicle Application.
␣SA's 912-pound "butterfly" for night-and-day
␣forecasting. Nimbus is a second-generation weather
␣e, based on successes achieved in the TIROS project.
␣Beginning with Nimbus 2 in 1966, this series makes instant
weather photos available even at night, through infrared
cameras that take photographs in darkness and send them to
simple and comparatively inexpensive ground equipment. (Its
predecessor, Nimbus 1, which had a twenty-eight-day orbital
life in 1964, could send night photos to only a few stations
having expensive equipment.)

Nimbus 2 was orbited May 15, 1966, from the Air Force
Western Test Range (Vandenberg Air Force Base), aboard
a Thrust-Augmented Thor with an Agena B upper stage. The
spacecraft travels from pole to pole in a 690-mile-high sun-
synchronous orbit (taking photos at about noon—local sun
time—and midnight). It completes each orbit in about 107
minutes. Photos are supplied to 150 stations, 44 of which are
situated in twenty-six foreign countries.

The Nimbus stands 10 feet tall, is 11 feet wide, and has a
5-foot-diameter ring containing sensory equipment. NASA's
Goddard Space Flight Center is responsible for project management. General Electric's Spacecraft Department is the contractor for integration and test. RCA's Astro Electronics
Division provides the advanced vidicon camera substation,
automatic picture transmission camera, and other equipment.
See *automatic picture transmission.*

nomenclature. NASA designates a spacecraft by a letter before launching (such as Biosatellite A), and then numbers the
spacecraft if the launching succeeds (making it Biosatellite I).

NASA usually uses Latin numerals as, for instance, with
the Saturn V rocket and the Explorer XXXIII spacecraft. Because Latin numerals become unwieldy, particularly in headlines and in tables, many leading newspapers, magazines, and
reference books switch entirely to Arabic numbers (Saturn 5
and Explorer 33). This practice also assures uniformity in
text that includes, for instance, the Soviet Cosmos 135 satel-

lite and NASA's Apollo/Saturn 202 spacecraft and launch vehicle.

NRD. See *National Range Division.*

Nuclear Detection (Vela) Satellites (NDS). Serving as the 007's of the heavens, NDS pairs were launched in 1963, 1964, and 1965 to provide full surveillance of the shadowed and sunlit portions of earth and space. To do so, they circle the earth in pairs, about 180° apart and 55,000 nautical miles high, in four-day orbits. TRW Systems built the satellites for the Air Force Space Systems Division, which manages the NDS—or Vela—program for the Advanced Research Projects Agency of the Department of Defense. The Air Force reported in 1965 that the satellites "function in excess of expectations, gathering data upon which to base the design of a worldwide nuclear detection satellite system."

The Atomic Energy Commission and the Air Force disclosed jointly in 1966, for the first time, that the 1965 satellites were "improved models [able] to find and record clandestine nuclear tests near the surface of the earth." The AEC and Air Force explained: "Electromagnetic pulse detectors, optical detectors, and associated electronic systems are designed to observe fireball light and radio pulses emitted from nuclear bursts." It was disclosed in 1966 that the 1967 NDS would be "continuously earth-oriented and downward looking [with] more sophisticated optical and electromagnetic pulse detectors capable of detecting nuclear explosions deep into the earth's atmosphere while retaining the space nuclear detection capabilities out to great distances."

The 54-inch-diameter twin NDS inspectors launched in 1965 were carried aloft by an Atlas-Agena launch vehicle and then separated in space by spring devices. At the first apogee, eighteen hours after launch, the first NDS was pushed to a 55,000-mile-high circular orbit by the firing of a basketball-shaped solid-propellant rocket. Fifty-four hours into the mission, when the first NDS had reached the opposite side of the earth, the second NDS was kicked into a 55,000-mile-high orbit by the firing of another "basketball" rocket.

The twenty-sided (icosahedron) satellites carry detection equipment supplied by the Atomic Energy Commission's Los Alamos Scientific Laboratory. It consists of a proton spectrometer and seventeen gamma ray, X-ray, extreme ultraviolet, and neutron detectors. The satellites reportedly can observe and record nuclear explosions as far away as Mars and Venus. The satellites, said the Air Force, "are not only providing the necessary background radiation data and scientific information on solar phenomena, but actually constitute an excellent test-ban monitoring capability."

Each NDS weighs about 524 pounds at launch and 334 pounds in orbit. Approximate weights of its units:

AEC detection equipment: 94 lbs.

Telemetry and communications: 44.2 lbs.

Electrical power and distribution, including 13,000 solar cells: 94.9 lbs.

Structure and propulsion: 69.6 lbs.

Expendables, including solid propellant: 21.9 lbs.

Nuclear Engine for Rocket Vehicle Application (NERVA). A joint technology development program of NASA and the Atomic Energy Commission, seeking to produce an upper-stage nuclear rocket for long-distance missions. Thrust of the proposed engine would be 75,000 pounds.

In a "milestone" test at Jackass Flats, Nev., in 1966, a NERVA breadboard engine system (an experimental setup rather than a flight model), was operated at full power of 1,100 megawatts for ninety-four seconds. The system attained a specific impulse over 50 per cent greater than that of advanced chemical rockets. Aerojet General Corp. is the prime contractor for NERVA. The Westinghouse Astronuclear Laboratory is a principal subcontractor and the Los Alamos Scientific Laboratory is performing basic work. See *Kiwi* and *Rover*.

OAMS. See *Orbit Attitude and Maneuver System.*

OAO. See *Orbiting Astronomical Observatory.*

Oberth, Hermann (1894–). Physicist whose contributions to space rocket technology included the pioneering work, *The Rocket into Interplanetary Space,* published in 1923. Dr. Oberth was born in Hungary (now Rumania), but did his most significant work in Germany. From 1955 to 1958, he served as an adviser in the U.S. Army's ballistic missile program. His book *Man into Space* was published in 1957. He returned to Germany in 1959.

Ocean of Storms. A dark, relatively smooth area of the moon where unmanned spacecraft—Luna 9, Surveyor 1, and Luna 13—made the first soft landings, all in 1966. The Ocean of Storms is not a sea, as has long been known, but has a surface that is sufficiently level and strong to support a spacecraft. It lies at the forward side of the moon (the left side, to an observer from earth's northern hemisphere) as the moon orbits the earth. A landing there permits a straightforward trajectory from earth.

oceanographic research (from manned orbiting spacecraft). The U.S. Naval Oceanographic Office and NASA's Office of Space Science and Applications are considering experiments aimed at enhancing oceanographic and marine technology research from manned orbiting spacecraft. Color photographs taken in the Gemini 4 and 5 flights indicated that valuable oceanographic data could be collected on earth-orbiting missions. Similar photographs from space could help oceanographers to delineate ocean currents, such as the Gulf Stream, or to study shoaling processes and river outflow into oceans.

ODRS. See *Orbiting Data Relay System.*

129

OGO. See *Orbiting Geophysical Observatory*.

on-board guidance computer. A light-weight, compact digital computer installed in a spacecraft to perform complex calculations for guidance and maneuvering. An on-board computer makes possible space rendezvous and docking, which are essential maneuvers on a manned trip to the moon.

For the historic first space rendezvous in which Gemini 6 overtook Gemini 7 at an altitude of 185 miles and a speed of 25,000 feet per second, the pursuing craft carried a 59-pound guidance computer. Built by the Federal Systems Division of International Business Machines Corp., the computer was able to perform more than seven thousand computations a second. Yet it required a space only about the size of a hatbox, or 1.35 cubic feet. It performed in thirty minutes calculations that would have taken a man twenty-four hours' work every day for four years.

"Gemini's computer is not particularly extraordinary in performance when compared with standard commercial computers," IBM said, but the miniaturization itself was extraordinary. Space engineers "shrank the specially designed unit down to a mere 59 pounds, designed it to use less power than a 100-watt light bulb, and sloped its sides to nest against the curve of the Gemini shell where it is part of the over-all guidance system."

In steering a spacecraft up to another object in space, man is operating on a fast circular track with no markings and he has no sense of "feel" on curves as does a racing driver. Under these conditions, man simply cannot perform the necessary complex mathematical functions fast enough for them to be of any use. Gemini 4 demonstrated this when, without benefit of a guidance computer, it fired burst after burst on thrusters and rose ever higher above the discarded booster it was chasing.

With a guidance computer, however, Gemini 6 smoothly overtook Gemini 7 and achieved a nose-to-nose rendezvous. The nose-mounted radar on Gemini 6 measured range, bearing, and elevation of its target. These details, plus data about altitude and attitude of Gemini 6, were fed into the computer, which determined the relative positions of the two vehicles.

The command pilot told the computer the angle of rendezvous by punching numbers on a manual data-insertion unit. Next he pushed the start-computation button. The computer then stated its maneuvering instructions on the incremental velocity indicator dial, telling how much thrust to apply forward or aft, left or right, up or down. With a maneuver controller, the command pilot fired his thrusters in the directions indicated by the computer and kept them burning while the numbers on the dial clicked down to zero. In the last, precise stage of rendezvous, the command pilot took over again with "eyeball" —visual—control to close the gap between the two craft.

On-board guidance computers also perform assignments other than rendezvous and docking. For instance, a 90-pound IBM computer is used to guide Saturn and Titan rockets. On a Titan 3 mission, for example, a computer steered from liftoff to orbit, started and stopped the transtage engines in space three times to achieve three different orbits, accomplished turn-around maneuvers in each orbit, and ejected an experimental communications satellite.

on-board stored data. Data recorded on magnetic tape in a spacecraft and later transmitted to a ground station on command.

orbit. The path traced by one body in its revolution around another body. In space flight, orbit ordinarily refers to a closed loop—the path of a spacecraft around the earth in an *ellipse* or, occasionally, in a *circle*.

To launch a payload into earth orbit, exactly the right amount of speed must be imparted to it. The payload must travel fast enough to keep from being pulled down to earth by gravity, and yet not so fast that it escapes from the earth's gravity.

An Uprated Saturn 1 launch vehicle provides an example of how an Apollo spacecraft may be put into earth orbit at the required speed—about 18,000 mph. (A speed of about 25,000 mph near the earth would put the spacecraft into an escape trajectory.) The first stage rises to an altitude of from 40 to 75 miles and attains a speed of 3,000 to 5,000 mph, depending on mission requirements. Then the stage burns out and falls away. The second stage ignites and carries the spacecraft

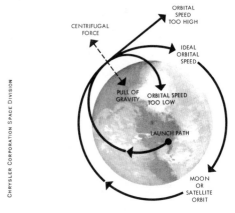

CHRYSLER CORPORATION SPACE DIVISION

higher and faster—but shuts down to coast to a point 350 miles high. In coasting flight, the vehicle (second stage plus spacecraft) arcs over under the influence of gravity and moves parallel to the earth. Here the second stage fires again and, with precise timing, gives the spacecraft its final orbital speed.

An orbit is described by its elements, including apogee and perigee, its period (time required for one orbit), and its inclination (the angle of its plane relative to the plane of the equator). The orbital elements of Gemini 7 included a 205-mile apogee, a 100-mile perigee, a 90-minute period, and a 32° inclination.

Orbit Attitude and Maneuver System (OAMS). A system of thrusters to control the roll, pitch, and yaw of a Gemini spacecraft. In addition, should the retrorockets fail, the OAMS thrusters would enable the Gemini to return from space by lowering the craft to the point where gravity would cause it to re-enter the earth's atmosphere. The system carries about three hundred pounds of fuel.

Orbiter. See *Lunar Orbiter*.

Orbiting Astronomical Observatory (OAO). An advanced unmanned spacecraft designed to give astronomers a clear look at the universe from above the obscuring effects of the atmosphere. The 3,900-pound observatory includes more than 1,000 pounds of scientific instruments, more than 440,000 parts, and thirty miles of electrical wiring.

The OAO's main body is an eight-sided cylinder, 10 feet long by 7 feet wide. Inside that body is a central tube 4 feet in diameter to carry the observing instruments. Solar panels extend 21 feet and make the craft look a bit like a bat.

Success of the spacecraft hinges on its ability to point astronomical instruments accurately at selected targets. Six telescope star trackers impart this precision by "locking on" to guide stars. Each star tracker is a 3.5-inch reflecting telescope mounted in two degree-of-freedom mechanical gimbals.

The first OAO was launched into a 500-mile circular orbit by an Atlas-Agena launch vehicle from Cape Kennedy on Apr. 8, 1966. Its power failed two days later, and no astronomical data were obtained.

In future potential, the astronomical observatory "ranks, in many respects, with the invention of the telescope," according to NASA. The agency has scheduled a series of four OAO's, with launchings about one year apart.

The OAO was developed by the prime contractor, Grumman Aircraft Engineering Corp. NASA announced in late 1966 that it was switching to a more powerful vehicle, the Atlas-Centaur, to launch future OAO spacecraft.

Orbiting Data Relay System (ODRS). A proposed system in which an earth-orbiting spacecraft (several hundred miles high) would transmit directly to a synchronous satellite (about 22,300 miles above the earth), which would relay the data to ground stations and control centers.

Because the spacecraft would be in constant view of the synchronous satellite, the ODRS would eliminate communications gaps experienced in the Mercury and Gemini flights. In those flights, contact was broken when a spacecraft left a ground station's electronic "line of vision" and was not reestablished until the craft came into view of the next station below its orbit. The ODRS would carry two-way voice communications and high-speed data. It also would serve manned and unmanned deep-space missions during the early trajectory.

Orbiting Geophysical Observatory (OGO). A heavy (more than 1,000-pound) research spacecraft that is called a "streetcar" because it carries more than twenty experiments as passengers.

Individual experiments are carried on a half-dozen or so booms jutting out from the body of a typical OGO. For this reason, the craft has been likened to a giant dragonfly or a scrapyard vulture.

A series of OGO craft study the relationship between the sun and the nature of the earth's environment. A complex sun-earth relationship affects such interplanetary space phenomena as sudden ionospheric disturbances, solar flares, solar wind, magnetic field disturbances, variations in atmospheric density, aurora events, and radiation belt particle populations.

The early OGO launches:

	Launch Date	*Weight (lbs.)*	*Orbit (mi.)* *Perigee—Apogee*
OGO 1	9-5-64	1,073	173 x 92,721
OGO 2	10-4-65	1,150	257 x 938
OGO 3	7-6-66	1,135	170 x 75,768
OGO 4	7-28-67	1,240	256 x 564

OGO's 1 and 3 purposely were put into lopsided orbits that took them close to earth and then far out to record the complete near-space scene. They provide simultaneous data from different locations in the earth's tear-shaped magnetic field. In contrast, OGO 2 was sent on a low-altitude, nearly polar orbit that, among other things, makes it possible for the observatory to record airglow and auroral emissions. OGO 4 also achieved a nearly polar orbit. (A polar OGO is also called POGO.)

The standard OGO has a rectangular main body six feet by three feet square and develops power from two large solar-cell panels that convert the sun's energy into electricity. TRW Systems developed the OGO under the technical direction of NASA's Goddard Space Flight Center. It is part of the scientific space exploration program conducted by NASA's Office of Space Science and Applications.

Orbiting Solar Observatory (OSO). An unmanned spacecraft that circles the earth at an altitude of about 350 miles—far above the hazy atmosphere—to study the sun and solar phenomena. With great accuracy, instruments on a "sail" can be pointed toward the sun. These include a coronagraph, an ultraviolet spectrometer, and a spectroheliograph. Other experiments are carried in packages in a spinning box, the other main portion of an OSO.

The 440-pound OSO 1 was launched in 1962, and the 545-pound OSO 2 followed in 1965. OSO 3 (627 pounds) was launched Mar. 8, 1967, and OSO 4 (599 pounds) on Oct. 10, 1967. OSO 4 made an ultraviolet chart of the surface temperatures of the sun—in effect, the first "color" photo of the sun.

Because the OSO's exceeded their six-month design flight time, all four were in operation simultaneously.

Ball Brothers Research Corp., Boulder, Colo., designs and builds the OSO spacecraft, and the Delta rocket launches them.

orbiting telescope. A proposed project in which a telescope would be carried on a manned earth-orbiting satellite. V. J. Vehko, director of engineering for the Chrysler Corp. Space Division, which is working on an orbiting telescope, commented: "Think what it would mean, for example, if you could orbit Mt. Palomar's huge telescope so its base would be 200 miles from earth. The resulting research would be fantastic. Telescopic observations will be vastly more accurate than any taken from earth through the dust-laden atmosphere. The resulting new astronomy in itself could well justify the space program effort."

Orbiting Vehicle (OV). The Air Force designation for five families (OV-1 through OV-5) of satellites that carry scientific instruments into earth orbit in the Aerospace Research Satellite Program. The program is directed by the Air Force Office of Aerospace Research (OAR).

The OV-1, which became the first to fly under the name of Orbiting Vehicle, grew out of a scientific pod program in which almost fifty instrument payloads were launched as "piggyback" riders on Atlas vehicles. The first OV-1 went into orbit in 1965 on the nose of an Atlas.

Builders of the families are: OV-1, General Dynamics; OV-2, Northrop Aircraft (using the modified spacecraft shell from the defunct Advanced Research Environmental

Test Satellite— or ARENTS—program); OV-3, Space General Corp.; OV-4, Raytheon Corp.; and OV-5 (or Environmental Research Satellite), TRW Systems.

OSO. See *Orbiting Solar Observatory*.

"out" mission (colloquial). A sun-orbiting mission outside the earth's orbit. Pioneer 7 made an "out" mission; in contrast, Pioneer 6 was placed on a solar orbit inside the earth's orbit.

oxygen, liquid. See *liquid oxygen*.

paddle-wheel satellite (colloquial). A spacecraft employing large solar panels to convert the energy of the sun into electricity. The electricity recharges the batteries that supply power to scientific instruments. Explorer 6, launched in 1959, was the first paddle-wheel satellite.

PAGEOS. See *Passive Geodetic Earth-Orbiting Satellite.*

parking orbit. An orbit around the earth, moon, or a planet achieved preliminary to making another move.

The Mariner 4 Mars probe used this technique when launched by an Atlas-Agena D into an interplanetary orbit. First the Agena D separated from the Atlas at an altitude of 115 miles, and then it restarted its engine to inject itself into a Mars trajectory.

The technique also will figure in lunar landings, as the Apollo spacecraft is to enter a parking orbit eighty miles above the moon to allow a lunar module to descend to the surface.

parsec. A unit of measure for interstellar distances. A parsec equals 3.26 light years, or 206,265 astronomical units.

passive communications satellite. A satellite that reflects a signal, but transmits none, as in the case of Echo. See *active communications satellite.*

Passive Geodetic Earth-Orbiting Satellite (PAGEOS). A 100-foot "balloon" satellite, similar to Echo 1.

PAGEOS 1 was placed in polar orbit on June 23, 1966, and became a familiar sight in the night skies, where it is as bright as the star Polaris. The satellite passes over each area of the globe twice daily—once at night and once in daylight—at an altitude of about 2,500 miles.

Although it carries no instruments, PAGEOS 1 is useful in measuring the earth because it reflects sunlight and serves as an orbiting source of light to be photographed from a network of forty-one ground-observation sites around the world. Over a projected five-year span, PAGEOS 1 often will be photographed simultaneously against a star background by two or more widely separated ground stations. The resulting collection of spatially oriented triangles will help to determine accurately the location of continents, islands, and other geographic points in relation to each other.

The aluminum-coated beacon was boosted into orbit by a Thrust-augmented Thor-Agena D launch vehicle from the Western Test Range, Cal. Its inclination is 86.9° to the equator. The PAGEOS project is one phase of the U.S. National Geodetic Satellite Program, which uses the principles of geometry to map the earth's entire surface.

payload. The spacecraft carried by a launch vehicle (or the instrumentation package carried by a sounding rocket). It is the essential freight and the reason why the journey is made.

Pegasus. A satellite named for the winged horse of Greek mythology, and aptly so, for its prominent wings measure 96 feet long by 14 feet wide. The wings are used to report punctures by meteoroids.

Three Pegasus satellites were launched in 1965 by Saturn 1 vehicles:

	Launch	*Orbit* (*mi.*)
	Date	*Perigee—Apogee*
Pegasus 1	Feb. 16	308 x 462
Pegasus 2	May 25	314 x 466
Pegasus 3	July 30	320 x 332

Although more than 1,100 punctures were recorded in the first twelve months of flight time, the conclusion was drawn that meteoroids in the near-earth environment present no great hazard to an adequately protected Apollo spacecraft on its way to the moon.

Aluminum sheets of varying thicknesses, or a total of 208 panels, cover the wings of a Pegasus. When a meteoroid penetrates a thin layer of copper bonded to the back of each exposed aluminum target sheet, the material removed by the impact is vaporized. This forms a conducting gas which discharges a capacitor, thus recording a hit. Fairchild Hiller Corp. designed and built the two-ton satellites. They were developed by NASA's Marshall Space Flight Center for the NASA Office of Advanced Research Technology.

perigee. The point nearest the earth in an elliptical orbit around the earth. Compare *apogee.*

perihelion. The point nearest the sun in a planet's orbit about the sun. Compare *aphelion.*

perilune. The lowest point in an orbit of a spacecraft around the moon. Compare *apolune.*

Phoebus (project and reactor). A project to develop advanced, higher power, graphite reactor technology. This NASA-AEC undertaking follows the Kiwi project that developed basic graphite nuclear technology. Through Kiwi and Phoebus, the Los Alamos Scientific Laboratory—the birthplace of the atomic bomb—is preparing the groundwork for nuclear space propulsion.

In the first full-throttle test of the reactor Phoebus 1-B, in February 1967, it developed 75,000 pounds of thrust and 1,500 megawatts of thermal power. See *Kiwi* and *Rover.*

photodissociation. "The removal of one or more atoms from a molecule by the absorption of a quantum of electromagnetic or photon energy. The energy of the photon absorbed by a system such as an atom or molecule increases in direct proportion to the frequency of the radiation. Simple molecules such as O_2, N_2, CO_2, H_2O, which are the primary molecular constituents of the atmosphere, can only be photodissociated by ultraviolet or higher frequency (shorter wavelength) light. They are not dissociated by visible light."—(American Institute of Physics)

photography. Working unattended in space, beset by the hazards of launch vibration, solar heat, and radiation, and restricted in size so that payloads are not too heavy, cameras nevertheless pioneer successfully in space. Three Rangers— 7, 8, and 9—sent back more than 17,000 TV photographs of the moon. Later the Soviets' Luna 9 and the Americans' Surveyor 1 photographed the moon from sites on the surface.

Then, in the continuing search for information on possible manned landing sites, the American Lunar Orbiters and the Soviet Luna series photographed the moon from orbit. Other cameras turn their eyes on earth (as in the case of ESSA and other weather-observation satellites) or on other craft in space (as in Gemini rendezvous maneuvers. As many as six cameras go on a picture-taking mission (as in the Ranger flights). Special features in space photography include the ability (as in ESSA) to store pictures on magnetic tape for later readout—in effect, delivery—to specialized ground stations in the United States.

photoionization. "The removal of one or more electrons from an atom or molecule by the absorption of a photon. As with photodissociation, ultraviolet or shorter wavelength light is required to photoionize simple molecules."—(American Institute of Physics)

photon. "The basic unit or quantum of electromagnetic energy. Although they have zero mass, photons have certain other discrete properties similar to particles in motion. Photons theoretically may be harnessed to power a spacecraft."—(Air Force)

photosphere. The surface of the sun, which is a layer of hot gases rather than a solid or liquid. The surface temperature is about 11,000° F.

PILOT (for *Pi*loted *Low*-Speed *Test*). See *lifting body* and *Spacecraft Technology and Advanced Re-entry Test.*

Pioneer. A series of deep-space probes, conducted from 1958 to 1960 and resumed in 1965 with Pioneer 6. Instrumented Pioneers collect information on the interplanetary environment.

Pioneer 1 (Oct. 11, 1958). This was the first U.S. deep-space probe. A Thor-Able 1 booster sent the 84-pound probe on a forty-three-hour flight 70,700 miles into space. Pioneer 1 determined the radial extent of the Van Allen radiation and made the first observation that radiation exists in the form of a band. It also made the first measurement of micro-meteorite density and the interplanetary magnetic field.

Pioneer 2 (Nov. 8, 1958). Rose to 963 miles, but the third stage failed to ignite and the probe re-entered the atmosphere.

Pioneer 3 (Dec. 6, 1958). Discovered that the radiation

belt is composed of at least two bands. Pioneer 3 was to have gone to the vicinity of the moon, but it reached an altitude of only 63,580 miles before it re-entered the atmosphere and burned up over Africa.

Pioneer 4 (Mar. 3, 1959). Was tracked for eighty-two hours to a distance of 407,000 miles and yielded information on radiation in space. Pioneer 4 passed within 37,300 miles of the moon and became the first U.S. spacecraft to go into orbit around the sun.

Pioneer 5 (Mar. 11, 1960). Made a brilliant exploration of interplanetary space between the orbits of earth and Venus. Pioneer 5 set a radio communications record of 22.5 million miles on June 26, 1960. It also contributed the first measurements of solar flare effects. Like Pioneer 4, it went on to become a sun orbiter.

Pioneer 6 (Dec. 16, 1965). This new 140-pound, drum-shaped craft became a sun orbiter and further altered man's knowledge of the sun and its atmosphere. It is a "spinner," and continuously scans a full circle in the plane of the earth's orbit. The "drum," 35 inches high by 37 inches in diameter, is packed with particle detectors, cosmic ray analyzers, magnetometers, and other instruments. It returned 400 million instrument readings in its first eight months of operation.

Pioneer 6's closest approach to the sun in its first year of operation was about 75.7 million miles. It surveys a strip of space about 40 million miles wide around the sun in the plane of the earth's orbit.

The discoveries of Pioneer 6 include (1) that the solar wind does not flow in a straight line and (2) that low-energy cosmic rays thrown out by solar flares surge through the solar system in well-defined streams.

Pioneer 7 (Aug. 17, 1966). Became a sun orbiter on an "out" mission, so that twenty-eight weeks after launch it reached a position 12 million miles outside the earth's orbit and 105 million miles from the sun.

Pioneer 8 (Dec. 13, 1967). Joined the two preceding sun orbiters.

NASA's Office of Space Science and Applications directs the Pioneer program. Project management is by NASA's Ames Research Center. TRW Systems builds the spacecraft a Douglas Delta rocket launches it, and NASA's Deep Space Network tracks it.

planetary entry parachute. A parachute designed to land an instrumented unmanned capsule on Mars or Venus.

Initial experiments in the planetary entry parachute program concentrated on developing designs and techniques for landings on Mars. In contrast to earth's sea-level atmospheric pressure of about 1,000 millibars, the atmosphere of Mars is believed to be only from 4 to 10 millibars—very thin for slowing down an entry capsule, which is expected to be shallow, conical, blunt-nosed, and fifteen feet in diameter. The capsule's velocity is expected to exceed 800 mph at the time the parachute is deployed.

The earth's atmosphere at 130,000 feet is believed to be comparable to that of Mars. It was at that altitude that NASA, beginning in 1966, conducted tests on experimental, parachute-equipped payloads that had been carried on sounding rockets and balloons. At 130,000 feet, small rocket motors accelerated the units of varying sizes and shapes to 800 mph to test parachute designs and materials. NASA's Langley Research Center managed the tests, which were held at White Sands Missile Range, N.M. The program was co-ordinated with NASA's Jet Propulsion Laboratory, manager of the Voyager project for planetary exploration.

planetary motions. The calculation of flight paths to other planets rests in part on the work of Johannes Kepler (1571–1630), German astronomer and mathematician, who established three laws describing planetary motions. Kepler's laws provided the basis for the formulation of the laws of gravitation and motion by Sir Isaac Newton (1642–1727), English mathematician.

Kepler's laws may be stated as follows:

1. The orbit of a planet is an ellipse with the sun at one focus.

2. The line joining a planet to the sun (the radius vector) sweeps out equal areas in equal periods of time.

3. The square of a planet's period of revolution is proportional to the cube of its mean distance from the sun.

planetoid. See *asteroid*.

Pluto. The outermost planet in the solar system, making a circuit around the sun once in 248.4 years. Pluto ranges from 2.8 billion to 4.6 billion miles from the sun. However, future spacecraft could be tracked all the way to Pluto by the 210-foot Goldstone antenna. Pluto has a diameter of only 3,600 miles. Its orbit is tilted slightly more than 17° to the plane of the earth's orbit (the ecliptic).

polar orbit. A flight path over the North and South Poles. The flight path provides north-south or latitudinal coverage; the earth's rotation meanwhile provides east-west or longitudinal coverage. A polar-orbiting satellite is able to "see" all of the earth's surface daily. A polar orbit may be combined with a sun-synchronous orbit. See *sun-synchronous orbit.*

Poodle. A small nuclear rocket engine being developed by TRW Systems. It offers low weight and low thrust (0.25 pound), and high specific impulse (in the 700 to 800 second range). These capabilities would greatly extend the range of interplanetary missions in the solar system. The radioisotope-heated engine is a direct-cycle unit that employs thermal energy generated by isotopic decay to heat hydrogen. The engine has been successfully tested in a laboratory of the Atomic Energy Commission, which is working with the Air Force on the project.

practical satellites. See *unmanned spacecraft.*

Precision Recovery Including Maneuvering Entry (PRIME). An Air Force program of 1966-67 in which three SV-5 unmanned vehicles were tested. See *SV-5.*

pressure suit (or **spacesuit**). A garment that provides an astronaut with his own environment, having a pressure higher than surrounding pressure. It enables him to work and move normally, or nearly so, under low-pressure conditions, either in or out of a vehicle in space.

Suits vary in construction to fulfill special purposes. The suit that Edward H. White II wore for the first U.S. space walk included a special outer layer and two external visors for protection against micrometeoroids, heat, and cold. The outer layer, weighing about 3.75 pounds, consisted of aluminized Mylar and felt covered with nylon. White's inner visor was made of Lexan, thirty times stronger than the plastic used in aircraft canopies. His outer visor was tinted to guard against glare. This and other Gemini suits were developed by the Crew Systems Division of the Manned Spacecraft Center. The David Clark Co. was the prime contractor.

Each Gemini 5 and 6 crew member wore a five-layer, full-pressure garment and helmet with mechanically sealed visor. The suit consisted of the following layers: (1) a white cotton constant-wear garment; (2) a blue nylon comfort layer; (3) the pressure garment, a black neoprene-coated nylon; (4) a dacron and teflon link net to restrain the pressure garment and maintain its shape; and (5) a white nylon outer layer to protect against wear and glare. Gaseous oxygen was distributed through a suit ventilation system, or "suit loop," to cool the astronaut and supply him with a breathable atmosphere of 100 per cent oxygen. An environmental control system provided the oxygen at 5.1 pounds per square inch in a pressurized cabin. If the cabin had sprung a leak and lost all its oxygen, the suits would have kept the astronauts safe by providing oxygen at 3.5 pounds per square inch.

For Gemini 7's fourteen-day mission, a lighter suit was developed. It consisted of only two layers: a pressure-retaining neoprene-coated nylon bladder and a protective outer layer of nylon. Even with a soft helmet and an aviator's crash helmet beneath, the outfit weighed only sixteen pounds. Designed for use only within a cabin rather than for space walks, this suit occasionally was depressurized and removed in flight. At other times the astronauts increased comfort simply by removing gloves and boots and unzipping the helmet at the neck so that it could be rolled back to form a headrest.

Fogging inside the helmet visor became a spacesuit problem in the second U.S. space walk. Eugene Cernan's vision was curtailed by fogging, and he had to cut short a strenuous physical effort to put on a backpack, or astronaut maneuvering unit.

For the Apollo missions, a new pressure suit was designed with an outside layer of white Beta fabric, a nonflammable fiberglass cloth. International Latex Corp. makes the Apollo suits, and Owens-Corning Fiberglas Corp. developed the Beta fabric. During routine flight (other than launch and re-entry), the Apollo astronauts were to wear light, unpressurized suits.

A hard spacesuit has been developed in several versions by

Litton Industries, Inc., contractor to NASA. The hard suit is designed to offer meteoroid protection with a honeycomb-stabilized shell and other advantages for extravehicular and extraterrestrial exploration.

pressurized. Pertaining to a spacecraft cabin, pressure suit, or other container: filled with air—or gas—at a pressure higher than the pressure outside the container.

PRIME (for *P*recision *R*ecovery *I*ncluding *M*aneuvering *E*ntry). See *SV-5*.

probe. A vehicle sent into space to gather information through instruments but not intended to orbit a planet or the moon. A probe may fall into a sun orbit, as did Pioneer 6 in 1966.

program. To pre-establish a series of events, as in "to program the Atlas-Centaur for booster cutoff at 150 seconds."

Project Apollo. See *Apollo*.

Project Gemini. See *Gemini*.

Project Mercury. See *Mercury*.

propellant. In a chemical rocket, the mixture of fuel and oxidizer—either liquid or solid—that is burned to provide thrust. (The term may also be applied singly to either the fuel or the oxidizer in a liquid rocket.)

A liquid rocket generally has separate tanks from which fuel and oxidizer are pumped into the rocket engine or engines, where they are ignited and burned. The hot gases created by combustion are expelled through a nozzle and thrust the rocket forward in accord with Newton's third law of motion: "To every action, there is an equal and opposite reaction."

In Project Apollo the Saturn launch vehicles use liquid propellants. In the first, or booster, stage, RP-1, a hydrocarbon resembling kerosene, is the fuel, and liquid oxygen (LOX) is the oxidizer. In the top stage, liquid hydrogen is the fuel, and LOX is again the oxidizer.

The RP-1 and LOX combination also serves in the first stage of the Atlas and Delta vehicles, but the Titan vehicles use other ingredients—and get a propellant that is hypergolic. The fuel is a 50–50 blend of monomethyl hydrazine and unsymmetrical dimethyl hydrazine (UDMH); the oxidizer is nitrogen tetroxide. The Agena upper stage, which operates in space, uses UDMH and a different oxidizer, inhibited red fuming nitric acid (IRFNA). A variety of other propellants, and a smaller number of oxidizers, also are available to propulsion experts.

In a solid rocket, the propellant is a rubbery mixture containing both the fuel and the oxidizer. Called the "charge" or "grain," this solid mass fits into a strong case that also serves as the combustion chamber. There is a "perforation," or hole with irregular edges, such as a cloverleaf design or a star shape, down the middle of the grain to improve the speed and evenness of burning. Upon ignition, the grain burns steadily from inside to outside, and hot gases are expelled out the nozzle. Once started, a solid motor is difficult to shut off. But "wafers," or segments insulated from one another, have been developed to facilitate control of burning.

Solid-propellant fuels include resins, rubbers, oils, and nitrates. Aerojet-General's 260-inch solid motor uses aluminized composite PBAN (polybutadiene, acrylonitrile, acrylic acid).

Both liquid and solid propellants may be employed in the same rocket. For instance, the Titan 3-C has a liquid core—the basic rocket—and three solid rockets are strapped on to impart a tremendous increase in thrust at liftoff. See *cryogenic propellants* and *hypergolic fuel*.

propulsion systems. Engines and associated equipment required for propelling a space vehicle. Propulsion by liquid rockets involves "the application of mechanical design, fluid mechanics, and thermochemistry to the technology of reactive propulsion employing liquid or gaseous propellants." That description is provided by the American Institute of Aeronautics and Astronautics to cover the scope of its liquid rockets technical committee. In space propulsion, other AIAA technical committees deal with launch vehicles, solid rockets, electric propulsion, and nuclear propulsion.

Proton. A 13-ton USSR satellite. In 1965 the Soviets shattered all records for satellite size by orbiting Proton 1 and Proton 2. They circled the earth at an altitude ranging from 125 to 375 miles and studied cosmic rays, gamma rays, and high-energy electrons.

Q

qualify. To verify performance by testing a spacecraft. The first Mercury spacecraft was launched unmanned in suborbital flight to qualify it for use in manned flights.

radar (for *ra*dio *d*etection *a*nd *r*anging). This term applies both to the technique and the equipment for determining the distance and the direction of objects by sending and receiving radio frequency energy.

radiation pressure. "The force exerted by electromagnetic radiation on a surface which reflects or absorbs it. Usually negligible, amounting to only a millionth of an ounce per square foot for sunlight on a black surface, it can nevertheless produce observable effects on satellite orbits. Echo 1, with a large area and small mass, had had its perigee height changed by 500 kilometers [about 310 miles] per year because of solar radiation pressure."—(American Institute of Physics)

Ranger. Three Rangers in a row—numbers 7, 8, and 9—delivered cameras to the moon for the first successful deepspace live television transmission (before the hard landing occurred). The detail in the best pictures was two thousand times better than had been possible through earth-based telescopes. Craters as small as three feet across were photographed.

A summary of the successes which followed a string of six failures:

Vehicle	Launch Date	Impact Date	Photographs Transmitted
Ranger 7	July 28, 1964	July 31, 1964	4,316
Ranger 8	Feb. 17, 1965	Feb. 20, 1965	7,160
Ranger 9	Mar. 21, 1965	Mar. 24, 1965	5,800

Each of these NASA spacecraft weighed 300 pounds and was launched by an Atlas-Agena vehicle. NASA's Jet Pro-

NASA

pulsion Laboratory built the craft. The Astro-Electronics Division of the Radio Corporation of America provided the high-resolution cameras, which began their picture-taking sequence 13 minutes and 40 seconds before impact and kept shooting until destroyed by intentional hard landings. Six cameras were carried on each Ranger.

RCS. Re-entry Control System. See *Gemini*.

Real Time Computer Complex (RTCC). An information-processing system that gives NASA flight controllers and astronauts the information they need in time to make flight decisions. In a space rendezvous, for instance, the "real time" complex defines maneuver lines, which are time points at which to conduct a maneuver (such as height adjustment) within an orbit.

The RTCC is situated in NASA's Manned Spacecraft Center in Houston. It was developed by and is managed by International Business Machines Corp.

The equipment includes five IBM 7094 Model 2 computers, able to perform 25 billion calculations each mission day. In addition, five IBM 2361 core storage units store the world's largest computer program, consisting of 550,000 individual instructions.

On all missions, the RTCC constantly controls computer job assignments on the basis of what has occurred and what will be required in the future. It also is used to test critical ground-support facilities before and during flights.

Redstone (and Jupiter). Former military missiles that were modified to become space boosters used for important early launchings. The Redstone, lengthened and mated with solid-fuel upper stages, became the Jupiter C, which in 1958 launched Explorer 1, the first U.S. satellite. Modified again, it became the Redstone-Mercury, and in 1961 lifted Alan B. Shepard, Jr., and Virgil I. Grissom in suborbital flight paths.

The Redstone grew out of a secret Army missile project assigned in 1952 to a group of scientists headed by Dr. Wernher von Braun. By 1955 Chrysler Corp., as prime contractor, had delivered the first Redstone, a surface-to-surface ballistic missile, 70 inches in diameter and 69.5 feet tall. An intermediate-range Army-Navy Jupiter, 105 inches in diameter and 60.3 feet tall, was developed in a follow-on project. Both the Redstone and the Jupiter became operational tactical ballistic missiles and for several years were deployed by the U.S. to launching sites in West Germany, Italy, and Turkey.

In 1959 a Jupiter booster (Juno 2) propelled the first U.S. payload into a permanent escape from the earth. It was Pioneer 4, which passed the moon and went into orbit around the sun.

Designs developed and flight-tested on the Redstone and Jupiter live on today in the Saturn vehicles. The eight-engine first stage of Saturn 1 and Uprated Saturn 1 contains a cluster of propellant tanks—a 105-inch central tank (the Jupiter tank) and eight 70-inch tanks (the Redstone version).

redundant. Back-up or superfluous. Every Gemini spacecraft system affecting crew safety had a redundant feature (or an alternate method of achieving a particular purpose). For instance, there were two complete and independent re-entry control systems to give 100 per cent redundancy. See also *"majority rule" circuit.*

re-entry. The return of a spacecraft or other object to the earth's atmosphere. To return from space without burning up in a fireball, a spacecraft must pass through a "re-entry window" or "re-entry corridor." This is a precise area through which a spacecraft in a given trajectory can travel safely with the protection of its heat shield.

Re-entry is initiated by firing retrorockets, causing a rapid deceleration so that the spacecraft drops out of orbit. Twenty-eight minutes elapse from the time a Gemini manned spacecraft fires a retrorocket at more than a hundred miles' altitude until its touchdown or splashdown on an ocean. The sequence of events:

0 minutes: Fire retrorockets and jettison the retrograde section, leaving only the crew compartment for return.

14 minutes: Reach 400,000-ft. altitude.

16 minutes: Communications blackout begins as the fireball cuts off signals.

19 minutes: Initiate guidance.

20 minutes: Blackout ended.

22 minutes: Drogue chute deployed (50,000 ft.).

24 minutes: Main chute fully deployed (9,800 ft.).

28 minutes: Spacecraft lands.

A variable lift capability built into the spacecraft enables the crew to "fly" it to a selected landing point—in the case of Gemini 9, to within three thousand yards of the USS *Wasp*. See *Project Gemini*.

Re-entry Control System (RCS). See *Gemini*.

Relay. In Project Relay, NASA studied the feasibility of active communications satellites at relatively low altitudes. There were two launches:

	Launch Date	*Weight (lbs.)*	*Orbit (mi.) Perigee—Apogee*
Relay 1	Dec. 13, 1962	172	820 x 4,612
Relay 2	Jan. 21, 1964	184	1,298 x 4,606

The Relay satellites were designed and built by the Astro-Electronics Division of the Radio Corporation of America under contract with NASA's Goddard Space Flight Center. Both satellites handled wide-band experiments (television) and narrow-band experiments (voice, facsimile, and teleprint). An outstanding event for Relay 1 was its international broadcast of TV pictures of events surrounding the assassination of President Kennedy. Relay 2 has relayed voices from Spain to Scandinavia.

The relay satellites also gathered scientific information on low-altitude flight. It was discovered that radiation damaged

Relay 1's positive-on-negative solar cells. Consequently, Relay 2 was built with negative-on-positive solar cells to increase resistance to damage.

rendezvous. As used in space flight: the complex feat of bringing two spacecraft together. The ability to effect a rendezvous is essential to a manned lunar journey, so that the Lunar Module can rejoin the Apollo spacecraft for the return to earth. Rendezvous also will be an essential part of assembling and using space stations for advanced missions.

The first rendezvous in space took place in 1965 when Walter M. Schirra and Thomas Stafford, in Gemini 6, overtook Gemini 7 some 185 miles above the Pacific.

Precise geometry is required if rendezvous is to be achieved. Gemini 6 started its mission in a 100 by 168 mile orbit, where it traveled lower than Gemini 7 and therefore faster (to avoid being pulled back to earth by gravity). Gemini 6 was required to "transfer" out to Gemini 7's orbit, overtake the higher craft, and pass in front of it on the fourth revolution.

At the peak of the second orbit around earth, a "catch-up" maneuver—firing thrusters as if stepping on the gas to speed up a car—lifted Gemini 6 higher, to a perigee of 134 miles. Then an "out-of-plane burn" yawed Gemini 6 to the right and gave it exactly the same angle of inclination as Gemini 7, or $28.9°$ to the equator. At the third apogee, the firing of aft thrusters (the second big catch-up maneuver) put Gemini 6 in a circular orbit at 168 miles. Still trailing Gemini 7 by about 185 miles, Gemini 6 obtained a radar "lock" on Gemini 7 at that point. Then Gemini 6 used an on-board guidance computer to determine how much thrust to apply in each direction—forward or aft, left or right, up or down. In what is known as the "terminal phase maneuver," small bursts were fired at intervals to close the gap. Finally, Gemini 6 moved out ahead of and above Gemini 7. There, flying backward, Gemini 7 fired forward thrusters to permit a slow final closing for a nose-to-nose meeting.

research grants and contracts. In addition to using its own research and that of industry, NASA taps the talents of the nation's academicians by awarding research grants and contracts to universities, colleges, and private research institutions. The following awards are presented here as a random selection out of hundreds to indicate some areas of co-operation between NASA and the academic world, and also to show the complexity of space research.

Massachusetts Institute of Technology: "Development of Decision-Making Devices Inspired by Animal Nervous Systems."

University of Wisconsin: "Multidisciplinary Research in Space Science and Engineering with Special Emphasis on Theoretical Chemistry."

Stanford University: "Investigation of Laser Dynamics, Modulation, and Control of Means of Intra-Cavity Time Varying Perturbation."

Rand Corporation: Development of procedures for examining the economic implication of manned space exploration.

research services. NASA makes available to scientists and to the general public a store of information that contains more than 235,000 titles on science and technology in space and aeronautics. The agency's Office of Technology Utilization has prepared a twenty-four page booklet, "How to Use NASA's Scientific and Technical Information System." It is available for twenty cents from the Superintendent of Documents, U.S. Government Printing Office, Washington, D.C. 20402.

retrograde motion. Orbital motion opposite to the normal direction. An earth satellite launched at an inclination greater than 90° will travel westward, or opposite to the earth's rotation.

retrorockets. Small rockets fired in the direction opposite to a vehicle's motion, thus slowing it down.

reuseable vehicles. Because of the great cost of vehicles, space administrators are interested in developing reusable launch vehicles and spacecraft. In 1967 the Lockheed-California Co. worked on a NASA contract for a study of an advanced air-breathing launch vehicle that would be able to cruise. The projected vehicle would make a conventional take-off with an aircraft-like first stage, using liquid hydrogen as a fuel. In space, the vehicle would be powered by an expendable second stage—a liquid-hydrogen rocket that could place a 50,000-pound payload into low earth orbit. At the end of a mission, the first stage would make a conventional horizontal landing.

For manned flight, various lifting bodies are undergoing tests as reuseable spacecraft. See *lifting body*.

revolution. A revolution of a spacecraft around the earth is completed each time the vehicle passes over 80° west longitude. This took about ninety-six minutes on a Gemini flight. But an earth orbit—a trip around the earth in an orbit—is space referenced and in Gemini took only about ninety minutes. NASA has explained the difference between a revolution and an orbit as follows:

"The longer time for revolutions is caused by the earth's rotation. As the spacecraft circles the earth, the earth moves about 22.5 degrees in the same direction. Although the spacecraft completes the orbit in about 90 minutes, it takes another 6 minutes for the spacecraft to reach 80 degrees west longitude and complete a revolution. Gemini completes 16 orbits per day, but in 24 hours crosses the 80th meridian of longitude 15 times—hence 15 revolutions per day."

Revolution also refers to the motion of a celestial body in its orbit; thus, "the earth revolves about the sun annually."

RL-10. A liquid-hydrogen-fueled engine built by the Pratt & Whitney Division of United Aircraft Corp. The RL-10 develops 15,000 pounds of thrust. It is used on the upper stage Centaur (two engines) and as the second stage (S-4) of Saturn 1 (six engines). The RL-10 was the first high-energy engine developed for the space program and the first to be flown successfully in space.

rotation. "The turning of a body about an axis within the body, as the daily rotation of the earth."—(NASA)

When a spacecraft is launched in the same direction as the earth rotates, it takes advantage of the velocity imparted by the rotation, which is about 911 mph.

Rover (project). A joint program by NASA and the Atomic Energy Commission to develop nuclear rocket propulsion. Project Rover involves the development of a reactor and an engine using the reactor as a heat source. Development is based on nuclear fission (atom splitting) in a reactor to heat a working fluid, which in this research is liquid hydrogen.

From 1958 through 1964, a series of eight Kiwi ground-based reactors—named for a flightless bird—was tested to develop a design for a nuclear reactor. In 1964 the last Kiwi was operated for eight minutes at 1,000 megawatts. Phoebus, a ground-based graphite-core reactor, underwent successful test firings in 1965 and 1967.

Nerva (acronym for Nuclear Engine for Rocket Vehicle Application) is a program to develop a rocket engine powered by a reactor. See *Kiwi, Nerva* and *Phoebus.*

The need for shielding against radiation creates a weight problem for designers of nuclear spacecraft. Dr. Wernher von Braun has forecast that "not too far in the future, huge nuclear-propelled spacecraft will take crews on long voyages deep into space. . . . The problems of man-made radiation connected with these space ships will prove far more challenging in the long run than those of the natural radiation in space."

Commenting on the future of nuclear propulsion, Harold B. Finger, manager of the NASA-AEC Space Nuclear Propulsion Office in 1964, said after the Kiwi reactor tests of that year: "We have proved that the nuclear rockets can give the kind of performance that is needed for advanced space missions. We could use essentially this type of reactor for experimental flights in the early 1970's and have an operational system by 1975."

RP-1. A hydrocarbon fuel resembling kerosene.

RTCC. See *Real Time Computer Complex.*

Samos. See *Satellite and Missile Observation Systems.*

San Marco. A 254-pound spherical satellite, 26 inches in diameter, designed, built, and launched (in 1964) by Italians. San Marco was the first satellite put up by another nation as part of NASA's international program. Previously, only Soviet and American crews had launched satellites. Using a four-stage Scout rocket at Wallops Station, Va., the Italians sent San Marco into a 124-by-490-mile orbit to measure communications interference and air density.

San Marco 2 was launched Apr. 26, 1967, from the Mombasa Platform in the Indian Ocean off Kenya. The Italian National Space Commission developed the range and designed the satellite, and NASA provided a Scout rocket.

satellite. An attendant body that revolves around another body (as the moon revolves about the earth) or a man-made object that revolves about a celestial body (as a Gemini manned spacecraft or an ESSA unmanned satellite revolves about the earth). Even though it is not yet in space, an object expected to be launched as a satellite is called a satellite (as an ESSA satellite on a factory production line).

Satellite and Missile Observation Systems (Samos). As their name makes clear, these are military reconnaissance satellites. The Department of Defense has not discussed them since 1961. Just before secrecy was imposed, a report said that the Samos was 5 feet in diameter, 22 feet long, and weighed 4,100 pounds. The payload was assumed to be cameras.

Saturn (planet). The sixth planet in distance from the sun. Three large, flat rings—looking much like a halo—make Saturn the most spectacular of the planets. Ten satellites surround Saturn. It is second only to Jupiter in size in the solar system and has a diameter of 71,500 to 74,000 miles. Saturn is a mean distance of 887 million miles from the sun and requires 29.5 years to make a revolution around it.

Saturn (launch vehicle). A family of the largest U.S. launch vehicles, developed by NASA with the goal of sending astronauts to the moon in Project Apollo. Three versions bear the name.

Saturn 1 (total thrust: 1,590,000 pounds) scored ten successes in as many launchings up to 1965, and its research and development program was then closed out. The launch vehicle with payload stands 190 feet tall (nineteen stories).

Uprated Saturn 1, formerly designated the Saturn 1B (total thrust: 1,800,000 pounds), began its flight tests in 1966. It stands 224 feet tall.

Saturn 5 (total thrust: 8,700,000 pounds), prime booster for Apollo missions, is under research and development. It stands 363 feet tall, higher than the Statue of Liberty.

As it is proved in flight, each version of the Saturn contributes to a successor. Saturn 1's first stage, given additional thrust, became the first stage of the Uprated Saturn—and it demonstrated that clustering of engines was feasible. The second stage of the Uprated Saturn 1 became the third stage of the Saturn 5—and it added to knowledge of how to handle liquid hydrogen as a fuel in space.

A stage-by-stage summary (with thrust in parentheses) shows how the U.S. increased its space capabilities rocket by rocket:

	First Stage	*Second Stage*	*Third Stage*
Saturn 1	8 H-1 engines (1,500,000 lbs.)	6 RL-10 engines (90,000 lbs.)	—
Uprated Saturn 1	8 H-1 engines uprated (1,600,000 lbs.)	J-2 engine (200,000 lbs.)	—
Saturn 5	5 F-1 engines (7,500,000 lbs.)	5 J-2 engines (1,000,000 lbs.)	J-2 engine (200,000 lbs.)

Rocket scientists at NASA's George C. Marshall Space Flight Center, Huntsville, Ala., led by Dr. Wernher von Braun, director of the center, guide the Saturn program. They have over-all responsibility for systems management and monitor the work of a large team of industrial contractors from coast to coast. In all, almost 300,000 people work on the Apollo/Saturn program.

Saturn 1. This 582-ton launch vehicle grew out of the Redstone and Jupiter boosters that scored notable successes in the late 1950's and early 1960's, but it develops many times more thrust because engines are operated in clusters.

Parts that proved reliable when flown in the Redstone and Jupiter have been incorporated into Saturn 1. Chrysler Corporation's Space Division, builder of the first stage of Saturn 1, reports that its central liquid oxygen tank is the same size (105 inches in diameter) as the old Jupiter booster tank. The eight smaller propellant tanks clustered around the central tank are the same size (70 inches in diameter) as the old Redstone tanks.

Dr. Von Braun's group of NASA scientists and engineers developed Saturn 1 on the concept of clustered propellant tanks and interconnected engines so that fuel would flow freely as needed and a mission could be fulfilled even if an engine shut down prematurely. Chrysler was assigned the job of building the first stage, for which North American Aviation's Rocketdyne Division supplied eight engines. Douglas Aircraft Co. was selected to build the second stage, for which United Aircraft's Pratt & Whitney Division supplied six RL-10 engines.

The record of Saturn 1's ten successful launches, all from Cape Kennedy:

SA-1 (Oct. 27, 1961): Flight of the first stage (with second stage carried inert) proved the feasibility of clustered tanks and engines.

SA-2 (Apr. 25, 1962): First-stage flight.

SA-3 (Nov. 16, 1962): First-stage flight.

SA-4 (Mar. 28, 1963): With one booster engine intentionally shut down, flight completed successfully.

SA-5 (Jan. 29, 1964): First launching with live upper stage. The liquid-hydrogen engines in the second stage burned properly for eight minutes, marking only the second time that liquid hydrogen had been used as a fuel in space. The orbited body weighed 37,700 pounds. It consisted of the spent second stage, instrument unit, payload adapter, Jupiter nose cone, and 11,500 pounds of sand ballast. This became the largest known orbited body. The payload alone weighed almost 20,000 pounds.

SA-6 (May 28, 1964): Boosted an Apollo boilerplate spacecraft (engineering test model) into an orbit with a 140-mile apogee. One first-stage engine shut down twenty-four seconds early, but the other seven engines burned two additional seconds to compensate for the lost thrust.

SA-7 (Sept. 18, 1964): Another Apollo boilerplate model was placed in orbit. This completed the development testing of Saturn 1 propulsion, structural, guidance, and flight control systems.

SA-9 (Feb. 16, 1965): Placed Pegasus 1, a 3,200-pound satellite, in orbit.

SA-8 (May 25, 1965): Placed Pegasus 2 in orbit.

SA-10 (July 30, 1965): Placed Pegasus 3 in orbit.

Uprated Saturn 1. The 647-ton Uprated Saturn 1, formerly called the Saturn 1B, develops considerably more thrust than Saturn 1 because of improved first-stage engines and a new, more powerful second stage. Its development began in mid-1962; flights started in 1966.

First stage: Rocketdyne uprated its eight H-1 engines by 12,000 pounds more thrust than in Saturn 1, to attain 200,000 pounds of thrust each. Thus the eight engines generate a total booster thrust of 1.6 million pounds. Chrysler, which produces the first stage, trimmed its weight ten tons by reducing the fin area, modifying propellant tanks, and making other engineering changes. The stage consists of nine propellant tanks, eight engines, eight fin assemblies and various control systems, structural assemblies, and intrumentation. It includes fifty-three miles of wire, 1,700 electrical components, and 73,000 electrical connections. More than twenty-four hundred subcontractors and suppliers from forty-four states worked with Chrysler on this stage 1.

Second stage: A single Rocketdyne J-2 engine, burning liquid hydrogen and liquid oxygen, delivers 200,000 pounds of thrust (in contrast to 90,000 pounds of total thrust from six engines in the second stage of Saturn 1). The J-2 ignites at about 2.5 minutes into a mission and burns for about 7.5 minutes. Douglas Aircraft Co. manufactures the second stage.

Besides the J-2 engine, the second stage consists of a propellant tank with a common bulkhead to separate the liquid hydrogen from the liquid oxygen, forward and aft skirts, thrust structure, after interstage assemblies, auxiliary propulsion system, propellant utilization system, stage separation system, and ordnance systems.

The Uprated Saturn 1 flew its first test on Feb. 26, 1966, and met all objectives. It lobbed a 45,900-pound Apollo

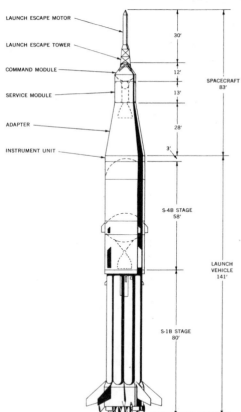

LAUNCH ESCAPE MOTOR

LAUNCH ESCAPE TOWER

COMMAND MODULE

SERVICE MODULE

ADAPTER

INSTRUMENT UNIT

30'

12'

13'

28'

3'

SPACECRAFT
83'

S-4B STAGE
58'

LAUNCH
VEHICLE
141'

S-1B STAGE
80'

NASA

spacecraft five thousand miles down the Eastern Test Range in a thirty-nine-minute suborbital flight from Cape Kennedy. This flight was designated Apollo/Saturn 201 (or AS-201).

On July 5, 1966, the second Uprated Saturn 1 mission was also a complete success. A total weight of almost thirty tons —including ten tons of liquid hydrogen—was placed in orbit. The primary purpose of this mission was to study the behavior of liquid hydrogen in orbit. This flight was designated AS-203.

The Uprated Saturn 1 was also employed as follows:

AS-202 (Aug. 25, 1966): Launched an unmanned Apollo spacecraft on a suborbital flight to test a heat shield.

AS-204 (Jan. 22, 1968): Launched an unmanned Apollo lunar module for its first test in space. The AS-204 originally was to have boosted the first manned Apollo mission in February 1967. It was undamaged in the fire that killed three Apollo astronauts on Jan. 27, 1967, and was moved from Launch Complex 34 to Launch Complex 37 to boost the first lunar module.

NASA scheduled these additional uses for the Uprated Saturn 1:

AS-206: Second unmanned flight test of lunar module in earth orbit.

AS-205: First Apollo manned flight, to test the command and service modules.

Saturn 5. This is the "moon rocket." With a thunderous roar, the first Saturn 5 lifted off the pad at NASA's John F. Kennedy Space Center, Fla., on Nov. 7, 1967. It stood 363 feet tall and weighed 6,220,025 pounds, fully fueled. In its first mission, designated Apollo 4, the "moon rocket" had an unmanned Apollo spacecraft aboard, and it placed 278,699 pounds in orbit 117 miles above the earth.

The second Saturn 5 rocket was launched on Apr. 4, 1968. It encountered disappointing engine troubles: two engines in the second stage shut down too soon, and the third-stage engine failed to reignite. Nevertheless, the mission, designated Apollo 6, was completed, as the spacecraft propelled itself to an altitude of 13,800 miles and made its planned high-speed plunge into the Pacific Ocean.

The first stage (S-1C) consisted of five Rocketdyne F-1

engines, each of them delivering 1.5 million pounds of thrust. They burn RP-1 kerosene (214,200 gallons) and liquid oxygen (346,400 gallons), the traditional fuels for a first stage in the Saturn family. The next two stages—ignited in space—burn liquid hydrogen. Its oxidizer is liquid oxygen. J-2 engines power both upper stages, with a cluster of five engines in the second stage and a single engine in the top stage.

Contractors for the stages are three old-line aviation companies, two of which entered mergers in the mid-1960's— Boeing (S-1C or first), North American Rockwell (S-2 or second), and McDonnell Douglas (S-4B or third). See also *Apollo.*

Saturn instrument unit. A 3-foot-high, 22-foot-diameter slice of the Uprated Saturn 1 and Saturn 5 launch vehicles. The instrument unit serves as the nerve center of the vehicle, for it navigates, generates steering commands, starts and stops engines and drops off stages, and communicates the vehicle's position and other information to the ground. On Saturn 5's moon mission, the instrument unit will inject the spacecraft into a lunar transfer trajectory.

Situated between the upper stage and the Apollo payload, the instrument unit consists of six major systems—guidance, flight control, environmental control, electrical, instrumentation, and structural.

As Saturn ascends from the launch pad, an International Business Machines Corp. digital computer within the instrument unit receives raw information on speed and altitude from the data adapter. The computer compares this raw information with an internally stored program and calculates the thrust direction so that the vehicle arrives at the required point of velocity and altitude. Steering signals are issued through an analog computer, which considers vehicle stresses and makes certain that no engine-steering command exceeds the design limits of the vehicle.

NASA's Marshall Space Flight Center and associated contractors designed the instrument unit. MFSC and IBM were jointly responsible for the early units, and IBM gradually assumed over-all responsibility for assembling and testing later units.

Scanner. A spacecraft to perform research experiments on the nature of the horizon as seen from space. The experiments, beginning in 1966, were designed to give NASA information that will enable it to develop better controls for future spacecraft. Scanner was the first spacecraft on which Honeywell was the prime contractor.

scientific satellites. See *unmanned spacecraft*.

Score (project). A U.S. Army communications satellite which won fame by becoming the first to transmit a human voice from space. It was a recording of President Dwight D. Eisenhower's Christmas message, beamed to earth on Dec. 19, 1958. An Air Force Atlas went into orbit with the satellite. The whole vehicle was informally known as the "talking Atlas."

Scout. A multistage launch vehicle with four solid-propellant rocket motors. The Scout is a versatile, low-cost launcher for small scientific payloads on orbital, space probe, and re-entry missions, including many Explorer and classified Department of Defense shots. It can place a 320-pound satellite into a 300-nautical-mile earth orbit or can carry a 100-pound scientific probe 18,000 miles from the earth. Used by both NASA and the Air Force, the Scout makes easterly launches from Wallops Island, Va., and westerly and polar launches from the Western Test Range.

The Scout's four standardized stages serve as "building blocks" that can be taken "off the shelf" in whatever combination is needed to create a launch vehicle for a specific task. A 72-foot-tall Scout, weighing twenty tons at liftoff, includes the following motors:

First stage: Algol 11B (Aerojet-General). Thrust: 100,944 pounds. Burning time: 80 seconds.

Second stage: Castor 1 (Hercules). Thrust: 63,109 pounds. Burning time: 46 seconds.

Third stage: Antares 11 (Allegany Ballistics Laboratory). Thrust: 22,606 pounds. Burning time: 34.9 seconds.

Fourth stage: Altair 11 (Allegany Ballistics Laboratory). Thrust: 6,416 pounds. Burning time: 22.2 seconds.

A combination of aerodynamic surfaces, jet vanes, and hydrogen peroxide jets achieve control. Guidance is provided by a Honeywell strapped-on three-axis reference system.

Ling-Temco-Vought is the prime contractor, and the Air Force Space Systems Division supplies program management.

SECO. See *sustainer engine cutoff.*

secondary propulsion systems. Systems on a spacecraft to permit maneuvering, as contrasted to the primary propulsion systems of the launch vehicle. Secondary propulsion enables a spacecraft to move in six directions: up, down, left, right, forward, and rearward. McDonnell Aircraft installed three kinds of secondary propulsion systems on its Gemini manned spacecraft. They were the orbit attitude and maneuver system, re-entry control systems (two), and the retrograde rocket system, which slows the craft down to start re-entry.

SECOR. See *Sequential Collation of Range.*

sensor. "The component of an instrument which converts an input signal into a quantity which is measured by another part of the instrument. Also called 'sensing element.' "— (NASA)

A sensor serves as a technical means to extend man's natural senses. Thus NASA's Langley Research Center embedded sixteen sensors into the nose cap of a Scout payload sent into space to measure the rate at which the surface of an experimental heat shield ablated (receded or "boiled away") during re-entry. Twelve sensors were spring wires and four were of the "light pipe" type which obtain optical information. Telemetered data were sent to ground stations from the experimental heat shield.

The number of sensors on a satellite can be considerably greater than sixteen, of course. Sylvania Electric Products recommended to NASA that one satellite collect meteorological and oceanographic data from about twelve hundred sensors.

separation. The final step in a launching, the disengagement of a launch vehicle from its payload. In an Atlas, the firing of three explosive bolts accomplishes the separation within 1.5 seconds. Two solid-propellant retrorockets fire, slowing down the Atlas and permitting escape of the payload.

Sequential Collation of Range (SECOR). A geodetic or surveying satellite which, as its builder expresses it, "is changing the face of the earth." Cubic Corp. builds the 45-pound SECOR for the U.S. Army Corps of Engineers. The Army's measurements via SECOR disclosed that the Ryukyu Islands were a half mile southwest of where they were believed to be. SECOR sends out sequential signals that bounce off points on earth (the Ryukyu Islands, for example) and are measured by tracking stations on hundreds of passes so that distances can be determined with certainty.

service tower (also called a gantry scaffold or gantry). A self-propelled structure used to service a rocket during preparations for a launch. In effect, a service tower is a moveable skyscraper; for instance, the one rolled up to an Atlas-Centaur launch pad stands eighteen stories tall. Using an array of wiring, instruments, cranes, elevators, and other equipment, prelaunch crews service the rocket from the tower, using retractable platforms spaced ten feet apart vertically.

shroud. A cone-shaped shield that fits on the nose of a vehicle to protect against high temperatures generated by friction during ascent through the atmosphere. Then explosive bolts free the shroud, which opens like a clamshell and falls away into space. In the Gemini 9 mission, the shroud on the target vehicle, the ADTA, gained attention when the clamshells did not fall away but dangled half open. The shroud, astronaut Thomas P. Stafford observed, looked like "an angry alligator," and it thwarted the planned docking.

shutdown. The deliberate cutoff of an engine or cluster of engines in a stage.

sidereal. Of or pertaining to stars and constellations. There is, for instance, a sidereal year, which measures the exact period of the earth's revolution around the sun. It is 365 days, 6 hours, 9 minutes, and 9.54 seconds. A sidereal day is about four minutes shorter than the mean solar day.

Sigma 7. The Mercury spacecraft in which astronaut Walter M. Schirra made a six-orbit flight on Oct. 3, 1962, as a part of Project Mercury. Flight time was 9 hours, 13 minutes, 11 seconds.

Smithsonian Astrophysical Observatory. This observatory, situated in Cambridge, Mass., assists the space program by collecting orbital data on artificial satellites. The Smithsonian network has twelve Baker-Nunn cameras spotted around the world, and it also receives reports from volunteer teams. Its American camera stations are located at Organ Pass, N.M.;

Jupiter, Fla.; and Maui, Hawaii. The other stations in the network are at Olifantsfontein, South Africa; Woomera, Australia; San Fernando, Spain; Tokyo, Japan; Naini Tal, India; Arequipa, Peru; Shiraz, Iran; Curaçao, Netherlands Antilles; and Villa Dolores, Argentina.

SNAP. See *Systems for Nuclear Auxiliary Power.*

Snapshot. See *Systems for Nuclear Auxiliary Power.*

solar-electric propulsion. A proposed method for harnessing the sun's power to drive an interplanetary spacecraft—a virtual flying windmill. Giant solar-cell panels would convert sunlight to electricity and operate a set of small ion-chamber engines. After a feasibility study, NASA's Jet Propulsion Laboratory reported in 1966 that a spacecraft with 5,000 square feet of sun-catching surfaces offers exceptional potential for making a 300-day journey to Mars by the mid-1970's.

solar cells. Devices that convert energy from the sun into electricity to power an unmanned satellite. The standardized Orbiting Geophysical Observatory, for example, carries more than 30,000 solar cells mounted on two large paddle-like panels. Mounted on a shaft running through the main body of the spacecraft, the panels rotate automatically. The satellite's orientation changes to permit them to face the sun at all times. The solar cells provide about 500 watts of power in an OGO.

solar flares. See *Sun and solar system.*

solar wind or **solar plasma.** An ionized or electrically charged gas that moves outward from the sun at about one million mph. This solar wind is believed to consist of electrons and hydrogen, helium, and other ions. The solar wind establishes the interplanetary magnetic field by drawing out magnetic fields near the sun.

Knowledge of the solar wind was altered and enlarged in the mid-1950's by Pioneers 6 and 7, Mariner 4, the Interplanetary Monitoring Platform spacecraft (part of Explorer series), and the Orbiting Geophysical Observatories.

Through Pioneer 6, it was discovered in 1966 that the solar wind does not travel in straight lines. In reporting the findings of Dr. Kenneth G. McCracken, of the Graduate Research Center of the Southwest, at Dallas, NASA said: "Low-energy cosmic rays generated in solar flares stream through the solar system in well-defined streams, and the direction from which the streams come varies from hour to hour. . . . The sudden changes in cosmic ray intensity indicate a considerable patchiness in the distribution of cosmic rays within the solar system."

Peak speeds of the solar winds were recorded at 1,675,000 mph by Explorer 18, an IMP spacecraft, and at 1,636,000 mph by Pioneer 6.

solid rocket motors. Experimental solid-propellant rockets are now being built in mammoth sizes—in diameters of 120, 156, and 260 inches. Because solid-fuel rockets offer simplicity and comparatively low cost, they are being tested for possible use in putting heavy payloads into space for NASA and the Department of Defense.

Upside-down firings of large solid rocket motors began in 1964 when Aerojet General Corp. tested a 120-inch motor in Dade County, Fla., south of Miami, and obtained 600,000 pounds of thrust. In 1965, at Brunswick, Ga., Thiokol Chemical Corp. fired a 156-inch motor that produced 3 million pounds of thrust. In 1965 and again in 1966, Aerojet General fired a 260-inch motor which each time attained a peak thrust level of more than 3.5 million pounds. Flames rose 1000 feet and smoke rose 7,500 feet into the Florida skies in the tests of the biggest motors.

In the 260-inch test in 1966, the rocket's 60-foot-long chamber was anchored in a concrete silo and its 20-foot-long nozzle pointed skyward. NASA reported that the motor burned near peak thrust for 114 seconds before tapering off, and that its total useful thrust time was 129.9 seconds. Thus, in less than 2 minutes and 10 seconds, the rocket burned 840 tons of a rubbery propellant. The burning temperature reached 5,500° F. Despite the great pressure and heat, the only difficulty encountered was delayed operation of the quench system, which resulted in the charring of the nozzle expansion nose cone.

In the third and final test firing of the 260-inch motor, it produced 5.7 million pounds of thrust, on June 17, 1967, in Dade County, Fla.

The experiments are designed to demonstrate the feasibility of building and operating large solid motors. The label "short length" is applied to the 80-foot version, because planners envision motors from 120 to 200 feet long, depending upon their mission. The thrust level may rise to 5 million pounds. The 260-inch program was started by the Air Force's Space Systems Division in 1963 and was transferred in 1964 to NASA and its Lewis Research Center. The Air Force kept that part of the program which deals with 156-inch solid motors—regarded as the largest practical size that can be moved around on land for military purposes.

Even the task of igniting the 500,000 square inches of propellant grain in a 260-inch motor proves gigantic. It requires another solid rocket motor (with 250,000 pounds of thrust). The smaller rocket is fired into the nozzle throat, and its 80-foot-long flame instantly ignites the full length of the larger motor. As the larger motor begins to burn, at the rate of six tons of propellant a second, the smaller motor swings away on cables and falls into a pond. And there is an igniter for the igniter motor—a 100-pound motor that delivers 4,500 pounds of thrust.

The industrial team, besides Aerojet General as prime contractor, includes Sun Shipbuilding and Dry Dock Co., which built the rocket case, and TRW, Inc., which built the nozzle, made of stainless steel backed with aluminum honeycomb.

Salient facts about the 260-inch motor:

Weight: 1,862,000 lbs.

Diameter: 21 ft., 8 in.

Length: Chamber, 60 ft., 3 in. Nozzle, 20 ft., 5 in.

Thrust: 5.7 million lbs.

Propellant weight: 1,680,000 lbs.

Propellant: Aluminized composite PBAN (polybutadiene, acrylonitrile, acrylic acid).

Grain design: Cloverleaf.

Insulation: 10 tons of asbestos-filled rubber 0.3 to 4.5 inches thick.

Case materials: Maraging steel with a minimum strength of 200,000 lbs. per sq. in.

Burning rate: 12,000 lbs., or about 0.5 inch of propellant thickness, per second.

sounding rocket. A rocket designed to obtain data on the upper atmosphere. Some of these research rockets climb as high as

4,000 miles. Most of them, however, operate from 20 to 100 miles high—an area generally too high for balloons and yet below the minimum level for earth-orbiting satellites.

In a fairly typical series of launches in 1966, sounding rockets rose about 40 miles with instrumented payloads, which then descended by parachute and transmitted data on atmospheric pressure, density, and temperature. At the same time, precision radar tracked the payloads to determine direction and speed of high-altitude winds.

Sounding rockets are relatively inexpensive, and some are small enough to be carried by one man. These lightweights include the end-burning Arcas, 8 feet long and 4.5 inches in diameter, and the internal burning Hasp, 9 feet long and only 3 inches in diameter. In contrast, the three-stage Honest John–Nike–Nike solid sounding rocket stands 47 feet tall and weighs 6,500 pounds.

NASA's Wallops Station is a center of sounding rocket launchings. Participants include NASA's Langley Research Center, the Army, Air Force, Navy, and Environmental Science Services Administration of the U.S. Department of Commerce.

Soyuz. A Soviet spacecraft that was introduced in 1967 but crashed on its first manned flight, killing Cosmonaut Vladimir M. Komarov. Soyuz 1 was launched on Apr. 23, 1967, and made eighteen orbits in 26 hours, 45 minutes. The USSR said that the craft's main parachute became twisted during re-entry, and that the craft fell 7 kilometers, or about 4.3 miles, to earth. Soyuz 1 was believed to weigh about 15,000 pounds, and to have been equipped for linkup with a larger vehicle having a propulsion unit.

space. "1. Specifically, the part of the universe lying outside the limits of the earth's atmosphere. 2. More generally, the volume in which all celestial bodies, including the earth, move."—(NASA) See *aerospace.*

Space Electric Rocket Test (SERT 1). A NASA spacecraft built by the Radio Corporation of America to serve as a platform in space to test two types of electric engines. See *ion propulsion.*

The SERT capsule was kept to 30 inches in diameter and 28 inches in height, but 370 pounds of equipment—including the two engines before they were deployed to outboard operating positions—were packed into it. A 9-pound magnesium baseplate (pointing the way to space-saving design) supported more than 300 pounds of capsule weight. A four-stage Scout rocket sent SERT 1 on a 48-minute flight from Wallops Station, Va., to a point 2,000 miles down the Atlantic.

space gun. See *hand-held maneuvering unit.*

space power tool. A minimum-reaction, self-contained instrument developed by the Air Force Aero Propulsion Laboratory for repairing or doing maintenance work on a spacecraft in orbit. The problem is for an astronaut to loosen or tighten nuts and bolts without absorbing a reaction in the weightless environment of space. The space power tool has an electric motor that runs on silver-zinc batteries stored in the handle. The Air Force has explained its use: "The electric motor drives a planetary gear train to operate a spring-loaded inclined cam mechanism. The action tightens a nut or bolt; the reaction is fed back through the gear train at a slower speed and turns a counter-rotating barrel on the tool instead of the operator."

space station. For generations, the space station has been a visionary scheme—a platform established in space, an orbiting laboratory, a vehicle in which a group of men work as it circles the earth. Since at a space station the force of gravity to be overcome in launching a spacecraft is only about 30 per cent of earth's gravity, a space station could also serve as a place of departure (and return) for flights to the moon or planets. It would also serve as a supply and repair station. The shapes envisioned include rings, dumbbells, spheres, and modular designs.

By 1969 or 1970 the Air Force was to launch its space station, the Manned Orbiting Laboratory—a Gemini spacecraft with an attached cylindrical laboratory. The Air Force planned to use the two-man MOL in part to study man's adaptability and limitations during a long stay in space. See *Manned Orbiting Laboratory.*

For the early 1970's NASA was planning to place in earth orbit a "workshop" made from an S-4B stage (the top stage of a Saturn 5 rocket).

The USSR has disclosed no plans, but U.S. observers believed that it has planned major earth-orbit operations as a step to manned lunar and interplanetary travel.

Space Tracking and Data Acquisition Network (STADAN). A NASA network with ground stations in the U.S. and overseas to track and gather data from unmanned satellites. It has fourteen electronic stations that communicate with satellites by radio. It also has twelve optical stations that photograph satellites in flight.

"space treaty." A no-bombs-in-orbit treaty drafted by the United Nations Committee on the Peaceful Uses of Outer Space. The United States and the USSR announced their agreement on Dec. 8, 1966, after negotiations at the U.N. Eleven days later the United Nations General Assembly passed the treaty by unanimous vote. Formal signing took place on Jan. 27, 1967, when representatives of sixty nations gathered in separate ceremonies in Washington, London, and Moscow. (In fact, representatives of the U.S., Britain, and the USSR signed in all three cities.) The U.S. Senate ratified the treaty by an 88-0 vote on Apr. 25, 1967, and the Presidium of the Supreme Soviet ratified it on May 19, 1967.

The treaty regards space as "the province of mankind." Article 4 of the treaty provides: "States party to the treaty undertake not to place in orbit around the earth any object carrying nuclear weapons or any other kinds of weapons of mass destruction, install such weapons on celestial bodies, or station such weapons in outer space in any other manner."

The treaty does not forbid military applications in space. It would not halt military manned orbiting laboratories, spy-in-the-sky satellites that look down on other nations, or ferret satellites that listen in on another nation's communications.

space walk. See *extravehicular activity.*

spacecraft. "Devices, manned and unmanned, which are designed to be placed into an orbit about the earth or into a trajectory to another celestial body."—(NASA)

Spacecraft Technology and Advanced Re-entry Test (START). An Air Force program to explore the maneuverability of future spacecraft upon return to the atmosphere. One program phase, called ASSET, was completed in 1965. In another phase, the Air Force selected the Martin Co. in 1966 to develop a manned, lifting-body vehicle—a revolutionary rocket plane without wings. The lifting-body research includes a project known as PILOT (for Piloted Low-Speed Test).

spacesuit. See *pressure suit*.

specific impulse. "A performance parameter of a rocket propellant, expressed in seconds, and equal to thrust (in pounds)
divided by weight flow rate (in pounds per second.)"—
(NASA)

Specific impulse tells how much thrust is obtained from
one pound of propellant in one second of engine operation.
Thus in rocketry it is a measure of efficiency, just as "miles
per gallon" of gasoline tells a motorist how efficiently his
car is operating.

Most chemical-rocket engines have a specific impulse of
about 300 seconds, but upper stages that burn liquid hydrogen
and liquid oxygen obtain a specific impulse of about 400
seconds. For the nuclear rockets of the future, the expected
specific impulse ranges from 800 to 1,000 seconds.

spin-stabilized. Spun like a top. Spin stabilization prevents a
spacecraft from tumbling aimlessly. The operational spin rate
chosen for the TIROS, for example, is eight to twelve revolutions per minute.

Sputnik. The USSR's satellite series that opened the Space
Age on Oct. 4, 1957, when a basketball-size sphere became
the first man-made object placed in orbit around the earth.
(In the first headlines, some newspapers reduced "artificial
earth-circling satellite" to "baby moon." Soon all happily
accepted the convenient Russian code name "Sputnik," meaning "traveler" or "companion.")

Sputnik 1. The first Sputnik was a "basketball" 22.8 inches
in diameter and weighing 184 pounds. In the initial orbit, it
had an apogee of 588 miles and a perigee of 142 miles. At
an inclination of 65° to the equator, it circled the earth every
96.2 minutes. Sputnik's batteries died on Oct. 27, 1957. The
sphere descended into the earth's atmosphere and burned up
on Jan. 4, 1958, at the age of 92 days.

The USSR's feat of launching a satellite surprised the world
and accelerated scientific and technological progress, particularly in the United States. Yet, in the strictest sense, the in-
tentions of both the USSR and the U.S. to launch satellites
were known long in advance—even if they were not fully
comprehended. On July 29, 1955, the White House said the
United States would make satellite launchings in the International Geophysical Year; later in 1955 the USSR said it,

too, would fire satellites. In the summer of 1957 a Reuters dispatch from Moscow detailed the USSR's launch plans almost exactly as they occurred—but this advance story drew little attention.

Sputnik 2. On Nov. 3, 1957, Sputnik 2 was launched and carried a dog, Laika, in a sealed cabin. (From the first, the USSR preferred dogs as test animals in space, and the U.S. preferred primates). Sputnik 2 weighed 1,120 pounds, but most of that weight represented the last rocket stage, which went into orbit along with a bullet-shaped satellite. The craft had a long, looping flight—from 140 to 1,038 miles in altitude. It disintegrated in the atmosphere on Apr. 14, 1958.

STADAN. See *Space Tracking and Data Acquisition Network.*

stage. A propulsion unit of a rocket, complete with its own supplies of fuel and oxidizers. So that velocity can be built up by steps, rockets are built in as many as four stages, stacked one on top of another. Usually each stage is dropped, at its burnout or cutoff, eliminating unnecessary weight.

staging. The procedure in which a spent stage of a launch vehicle is separated from adjoining upper stages and allowed to fall away into space.

standard atmosphere. A hypothetical vertical distribution of atmospheric pressure, density, temperature, and other factors —in effect, a profile of the earth's atmosphere. By agreement, the hypothetical figures are taken as representative of the atmosphere for investigating the effect on spacecraft and aircraft operation and design, and for general scientific use.

The U.S. Committee on the Extension of the Standard Atmosphere (COESA) has published a volume, "U.S. Standard Atmosphere, 1962," tabulating and detailing the properties of the atmosphere up to 400 miles, and a sister publication, "U.S. Standard Atmosphere Supplements, 1966," extending the vertical profile to 600 miles. Tables in the two publications list information as related to latitude, day-night variation, season, and solar cycle. COESA is headed by co-chairmen from NASA, the Air Force Cambridge Research Laboratories, and the Environmental Science Services Administration. See *atmosphere.*

START. See *Spacecraft Technology and Advanced Re-entry Test.*

state of the art. The status of engineering and technical knowledge and capability in a given industry or group of industries.

static firing (or captive firing). Test firing of a propulsion system while the launch vehicle is held down on a test stand.

stationary satellite. See *synchronous satellite*.

stratosphere. "The region of the atmosphere lying on the average between about 12 and 60 kilometers [about 7 to 37 miles]; it has a temperature which is either constant or increases with altitude, and is therefore stable against convection. The upper part of the stratosphere is at a temperature of about 260° K and is heated by the absorption of ultraviolet light by ozone."—(American Institute of Physics)

streetcar satellite (colloquial). A standardized satellite that has the ability to carry many different experiments. A streetcar satellite such as the Orbiting Geophysical Observatory uses the same basic structure, power supply, telemetry and command systems, and thermal control for each spacecraft in a series.

suborbital flight. A flight on a ballistic trajectory for less than a full orbit.

Sun and solar system. The sun is a star, of less than average size, at the center of the solar system. Its diameter is 865,000 miles, and its mass is 99 per cent of that in the entire solar system. Its gravitational pull holds the system's nine planets —Mercury, Venus, Earth, Mars, Jupiter, Saturn, Uranus, Neptune, and Pluto—in their orbits. The orbits of all the planets, excepting that of Pluto, lie nearly in the same plane, and all nine planets move in the same direction around the sun.

The sun is a mass of heated gases, with a surface temperature that exceeds 10,000° F, but its center is far hotter—in the millions of degrees. Even though it is only an average star, its diameter is 109 times that of the earth. The sun's surface, the brilliant photosphere, is covered with dark areas, or sunspots, that show strong magnetic fields. Sunspot groups vary in number, but they reach a peak about every eleven years. Giant solar flares, which are sudden and temporary disturbances on the sun's surface that last up to several hours, release proton showers that may subject space travelers to lethal amounts of radiation.

Information on solar activity is gathered by unmanned interplanetary spacecraft and sun-monitoring stations on earth in efforts to develop a reliable system of forecasting that will assure the safety of space travelers. Before the United States and the USSR began manned earth-orbiting flights, there were suggestions that even short space travel might bring harm to man through radiation, but no evidence has developed to support these fears. Dr. George E. Mueller, NASA associate administrator for manned space flight, said reports show that the worst flares on record, in July 1959, would have inflicted only 15 per cent of the safe dose of radiation on the crew of an Apollo spacecraft had it been on a lunar mission at that time.

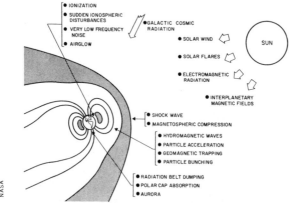

With Pioneer 6, launched late in 1965, NASA began the first systematic study of changes in phenomena in interplanetary space. The new Pioneers are surveying a strip of space about 40 million miles wide. Instruments aboard the Pioneers measure cosmic rays and the strength of the solar magnetic field. Other data on solar activity is collected by the Interplanetary Monitoring Platform (IMP) satellites of the Explorer series, by the Orbiting Geophysical Observatory series, and by Mariner 4, which, after photographing Mars in 1965, kept on traveling and communicating with the Deep Space Network.

Solar disturbances, along with events in distant galaxies, greatly influence space between the planets. NASA observed in 1966 that known phenomena in interplanetary space generally fall into these categories:

"Particles—Electrons and hydrogen and helium nuclei carrying an electric charge which make up the 'solar wind'; cosmic rays which are extremely fast moving or energetic charged nuclear particles of many elements; and cosmic dust and meteoroids.

"Radiation—The entire electromagnetic spectrum such as light, radio, and X-rays.

"Fields—Magnetic, electric, and gravitational."

The solar magnetic field appears to be "snarled" near the sun, and it becomes even more bent at greater distances when altered by the solar wind. NASA said: "The result is that the field lines of force, rooted in the sun and stretched through interplanetary space, are twisted about each other with kinks as tight as 90 degrees or more—like many strands of spaghetti in boiling water."

ṣun-synchronous orbit. A polar orbit in which a spacecraft passes over each part of earth at the same local sun time each day (about noon and midnight). Nimbus 2, a twenty-four-hour picture-taking weather satellite, achieved this orbit in a launch window open only from 12:45 A.M. (Pacific Daylight Time) to 1:58 A.M. A sun-synchronous, high-noon orbit gives Nimbus 2 maximum power for its batteries and maximum illumination for photographic purposes. The eastward drift of the NASA satellite is about one degree daily, at the same rate and direction as the earth moves around the sun. In daylight orbits, the sun is always behind Nimbus, even as a good novice photographer keeps the sun behind himself.

Surveyor. An unmanned spacecraft developed by NASA to achieve a soft landing on the moon. The objective of the seven vehicles in the Surveyor series was to gather lunar surface information needed for the Apollo man-on-the-moon program.

Surveyor 1, against incredible odds, set down softly on the moon's Ocean of Storms on June 1, 1966. From launch to touchdown the trip covered 247,538 miles and required sixty-three hours. In the critical final minutes and seconds, the soft landing was made with the aid of an array of equipment —a solid-propellant retrorocket and three liquid-fuel vernier engines, a flight programmer and analog computer, and radars to determine altitude and rate of descent.

The craft began transmitting television pictures and photographs immediately upon descent. "Overnight," said President Johnson, "the eyes of Surveyor 1 have become the eyes of the world on the moon." Surveyor 1 showed the world a flat landscape, desolate, strewn with rubble. By the time the lunar night set in, fourteen earth days later, the spacecraft had taken more than 9,000 photographs around the Ocean of Storms.

Surveyor is a three-legged craft standing 10 feet high. It weighs 2,194 pounds at launch, but only about 620 pounds when it reaches the moon, since a 1,377-pound retrorocket is jettisoned after burnout and additional weight is lost as propellants are expended. Significantly, Surveyor 1 did not sink into the moon's surface—an observation made when its scanning camera photographed one of the feet.

Hughes Aircraft Co. built the craft under contract to NASA's Jet Propulsion Laboratory. The launch vehicle was an Atlas-Centaur, burning liquid hydrogen in the upper stage.

The approximate altitudes and velocities of the last portion of the craft's descent to the moon's surface:

At 60 miles: Main retrorocket fires; craft is traveling at 6,100 mph.

At 25,000 feet: Main retrorocket burns out and is ejected; vernier engines take over; craft is moving at 240 mph.

At 13 feet: Vernier engines shut down; craft is moving at 3.5 mph.

Touchdown: At 10 mph.

Surveyor 2, launched in September 1966, crashed into the moon after an attempt to refine its trajectory failed.

Surveyor 3, launched April 17, 1966, landed successfully on the moon and sent back thousands of pictures of the lunar landscape. This craft had an extensible arm equipped with a shovel to sample the soil's consistency and weight-bearing potential. The lunar soil, NASA said, "apparently is similar to common volcanic rock of earth."

Surveyor 4, launched July 14, 1967, was unsuccessful because communications were lost in the last few seconds as the spacecraft settled down on the moon.

Consecutive successes were achieved by *Surveyor 5,* launched Sept. 9, 1967; *Surveyor 6,* Nov. 7, 1967; and *Surveyor 7,* Jan. 7, 1968. The first launch from the moon's surface was achieved when engineers on earth fired small control rockets on Surveyor 6, causing it to rise 14 feet and move 8 feet away.

sustainer engine cutoff (SECO). Shutdown of the center or sustainer engine in the ascent of an Atlas launch vehicle. The SECO command comes about 4 minutes, 41 seconds into the flight in a typical Atlas launching with an Agena upper stage.

SV-5. A lifting body—a rocket plane without wings—developed for the Air Force by the Martin Company, a division of the Martin Marietta Corp.

Three unmanned versions, the SV5-D's, were launched in 1966 and 1967 in a project that the Air Force called PRIME (Precision Recovery Including Maneuvering Entry). All were sent in a ballistic trajectory down the Air Force Western Test Range by an Atlas booster, but the first two vehicles were not recovered. On Apr. 19, 1967, on the third flight, an SV-5D was recovered in mid-air. Because all test objectives had been attained, a fourth launch became unnecessary.

A one-man version, known as the SV-5P (X-24A) was designed to be flown in an Air Force project called PILOT (Piloted Low-Speed Test). The SV-5P was designed to explore the maneuverability of a lifting body as a pilot decelerates from Mach 2 (over 1,000 mph) to a speed of about 150 mph. The X-24A was scheduled for flight tests at Edwards Air Force Base, Cal., in a joint Air Force-NASA lifting body program. See *lifting body*.

synchronous satellite. A west-to-east satellite placed at an altitude of about 22,300 miles above the equator so that it makes one revolution in twenty-four hours, as does the earth. Because it moves at the same speed as the earth, a synchronous satellite has a fixed position in relation to ground stations. In effect, it hovers over one spot. Three operating synchronous satellites are sufficient for a global communications system.

Syncom. An experimental synchronous communications satellite of the active repeater variety.

Syncom 1, although launched successfully in 1963, failed as a communications satellite because contact was lost permanently for unknown reasons just as the satellite was heading into a synchronous orbit.

NASA put *Syncom 2* "on station" over Brazil in 1963 and *Syncom 3* over the Pacific Ocean in 1964. Both achieved nearly stationary positions more than 22,000 miles above the equator. Syncom 2 moves in a figure-8 pattern 33° north and south of the equator, but Syncom 3 was adjusted so precisely in orbit that it moves less than one-tenth of a degree north or south of the equator.

Syncom 3 was used to carry a live telecast of the opening ceremonies of the 1964 Olympic Games in Tokyo to the West Coast of the United States, and both satellites demonstrated the merits of global transmission via a synchronous satellite.

A Syncom weighs 150 pounds, including a 90-pound rocket motor that kicks it into synchronous orbit. It measures 28 inches in diameter and 25 inches high.

synodic period (of a planet). The time between two successive conjunctions with the sun, as observed from the earth. The synodic period is important in determining the most opportune time for launching a spacecraft from earth to another planet.

Systems for Nuclear Auxiliary Power (SNAP). A program in which the Atomic Energy Commission, NASA, and the Department of Defense develop nuclear auxiliary power for use on board spacecraft. These systems operate communications, data transmission, and other internal equipment. Project SNAP consists of many undertakings, numbered as high as SNAP 50.

Nuclear auxiliary power first went into space aboard the Transit 4A navigation satellite on June 29, 1961. That project involved SNAP 3, a radioisotope-fueled thermoelectric power unit weighing less than five pounds.

The first flight test of a nuclear-fission reactor took place on Apr. 3, 1965, when SNAP 10A was orbited in a 970-pound satellite called Snapshot. The 210-pound SNAP reactor, about the size of a five-gallon tank, used uranium 235 as a fuel and was cooled by liquid sodium-potassium. Nuclear energy was converted to heat, which in turn was converted into electrical energy (565 watts) by a thermoelectric generator. The power ran the spacecraft's electrical circuits for forty-eight days, and then the power ceased.

TAD. Thrust-Augmented Delta. See *Delta.*

telecommunication. "Any transmission, emission, or reception of signs, signals, writing, images, and sounds or intelligence of any nature by wire, radio, visual, or other electromagnetic systems."—(Standardized for use by the Joint Chiefs of Staff, English Speaking Nations, and the American, British, and Canadian Air Forces)

telemetry. "The science of measuring a quantity or quantities, transmitting the results to a distant station, indicating, and/or recording the quantities measured."—(NASA)

In a typical telemetry system on an Atlas SLV-3 launch vehicle, electrical apparatus measures quantities such as temperature, pressure, acceleration, and deflections. These measurements tell how the engines are performing, how the propellants are being utilized, and how things are going in various systems, including guidance, hydraulic, pneumatic, and electrical. A thirty-six-channel telemetering package mounted on the Atlas broadcasts the data by radio transmitter to a receiving station at Cape Kennedy. There the Air Force and the Convair Division of General Dynamics, Atlas contractor, analyze and evaluate the data for use in future operations.

Television and Infrared Observation Satellite (TIROS). NASA's weather-watching satellites that since 1960 have photographed cloud formations and measured both solar radiation and the earth's heat radiation.

In their first five years of operation, TIROS satellites transmitted more than half a million pictures not only of cloud cover but also of storms, ice floes, and other weather data. Because of their ability to see so much of the earth's cloud cover, TIROS satellites have been called on for weather information to support manned space flights and Ranger and Mariner unmanned missions.

By 1966 the ten successful experimental TIROS satellites had been followed by ESSA 1 and ESSA 2, forming the world's first TIROS operational satellite (TOS) system. The system serves the U.S. government's Environmental Science Services Administration (ESSA), of which the U.S. Weather Bureau is a part.

The Radio Corporation of America builds the TIROS and ESSA, which has evolved into a hatbox-shaped craft that "rolls" like a cartwheel on its near-polar orbit. Two cameras are independent and redundant—either can provide all coverage. They send weather pictures to simple, desk-size ground stations within line of sight of the satellite as it passes overhead. See *automatic picture transmission.*

Telstar. Bell Telephone Laboratories, a subsidiary of American Telephone and Telegraph Co., designed and built Telstar 1 (1962) and Telstar 2 (1963), active repeater communications satellites. AT&T paid NASA for the launch vehicles, launching facilities, and initial tracking of these experimental, medium-altitude communications satellites.

Both demonstrated an ability to handle large volumes of different kinds of communications, including TV, voice, facsimile, and data. Both were used for live television broadcasts to and from Europe.

The two Telstars were similar 34.5-inch spheres, but the second version had additional refinements, weighed five pounds more (at 175 pounds), and was given a higher orbit, ranging from 600 to 6,700 miles.

thermosphere. "The region of the atmosphere, above the mesosphere, in which there is strong heating and increasing temperature, resulting from the photodissociation of O_2 and the photoionization of N, N_2, and O. It extends roughly from an altitude of 90 to 600 kilometers [56 to 373 miles]."— (American Institute of Physics)

think tank. See *brain bank.*

Thor. An Air Force liquid-fueled intermediate-range (1,500-mile) missile that first achieved that distance in a launch from Cape Canaveral on Oct. 11, 1957. A modified version of the

Thor became the first stage of many launch vehicles built by the Douglas Missile & Space Systems Division. In the 1960's it was combined with upper stages to launch satellites as a Thor-Able, or Thor-Able-Star, or Thor-Agena, or the Delta (a three-stage vehicle with the Thor as the basic stage). In some versions, solid-propellant rockets were strapped on to the first stage for extra thrust, so that the vehicles became known as the Thrust-Augmented Thor or Thrust-Augmented Delta. See *Delta* and *launch vehicles.*

Thor-Agena D. A two-stage liquid propulsion launch vehicle used by the Air Force for classified Department of Defense projects and by NASA for orbiting scientific satellites. See *Agena, Agena Target Vehicle,* and *Delta.*

thrust. The pushing force developed by a rocket engine. The push develops as propellants are burned in the combustion chamber and drive the resulting hot gases out of the nozzle at the rear of the rocket. For every action there is an equal and opposite reaction (Sir Isaac Newton's third law), and therefore the hot gases thrust the vehicle forward. The amount of thrust depends upon the propellant mass flow rate (determining how fast the propellant is burned) and upon the velocity at which the gases are expelled. Thrust is usually measured in pounds, at sea level. But sometimes it is measured "at altitude," as when an upper stage of a launch vehicle is ignited in space.

In a vertical liftoff, the pounds of thrust developed by the engine or engines must exceed the weight of the space vehicle if it is to oppose gravity successfully. An Uprated Saturn 1 launch vehicle with an Apollo spacecraft as a payload weighs 1,187,000 pounds, and so its engines must develop more than 1,187,000 pounds of thrust in the first (booster) stage to lift Apollo-Saturn off the launching pad. The vehicle's eight engines provide a margin of safety by developing 1,600,000 pounds of total thrust at liftoff.

Thrust-Augmented Delta. See *Delta.*

Thumba Equatorial Launching Site. An international launch range situated on the geomagnetic equator near Trivandrum, India, for scientific research with sounding rockets. It is open to all U.N. member states. The range was dedicated Feb. 2, 1968.

TIROS. See *Television and Infrared Observation Satellite.*

Titan. A U.S. Air Force intercontinental ballistic missile—a military weapon—that evolved into NASA's Titan 2 Gemini Launch Vehicle and the Air Force's Titan 3 Standard Space Launch Vehicle (SLV-5).

Titan 2 (Gemini launch vehicle). A modified Air Force Titan 2 intercontinental ballistic missile used to launch NASA's two-man Gemini spacecraft. The two-stage Titan 2 produces 530,000 pounds of thrust in two stages and hurls the manned spacecraft into an earth orbit with an apogee of usually about 168 miles.

Salient facts about the Titan 2 as a launch vehicle:

	First stage	*Second stage*
Height	63 ft.	27 ft.
Diameter	10 ft.	10 ft.
Thrust	430,000 lbs.	100,000 lbs.
	(2 engines)	(1 engine)

With spacecraft added, the over-all height becomes 109 feet and the combined weight 170 tons.

The launch vehicle uses storable liquid propellants that are hypergolic (that burn when the fuel and oxidizer come in contact), so that no ignition system is required. Countdown time is shortened because propellants remain in the tanks ready for ignition. The fuel is a 50–50 blend of monomethyl hydrazine and unsymmetrical dimethyl hydrazine (UDMH); the oxidizer is nitrogen tetroxide (N_2O_4).

Modifications made on the military missile to convert it to a launch vehicle include addition of a malfunction detection system and a back-up flight control for use if the primary system fails.

The Titan 2 began its manned flights on Mar. 23, 1965, when it sent Virgil I. Grissom and John W. Young on a three-orbit mission, and it continued to serve throughout the Gemini program. The Martin Co., a division of Martin Marietta Corp., builds the Gemini launch vehicle in its Baltimore Division. Aerojet General Corp. provides the propulsion system; General Electric Co., the radio guidance system; and Burroughs Corp., the ground guidance computer. The Space

Systems Division of the Air Force System Command directed the Gemini launch-vehicle program.

Titan 3 (U.S. Air Force Standard Space Launch Vehicle, or SLV-5). A launch vehicle being developed to perform a variety of heavy-duty manned and unmanned space missions. It will meet requirements for launching 12.5 tons into earth orbit or 2.5 tons to escape velocity.

The Titan 3 launch vehicle poised at Cape Kennedy.

The Titan 3 is flown in two forms, or configurations:

3A (SLV-5A). A basic "core" vehicle, consisting of Martin's two-stage Titan 2 plus a new upper stage and control module mounted on top. Thrust totals 546,000 pounds—430,000 in the first stage, 100,000 in the second stage, and 16,000 in the transtage (which provides a final kick to attain the exact orbit desired). The 3A stands 124 feet tall and measures 10 feet in diameter. The Air Force Systems Command has reported: "Development flight test of the Titan 3A, designated Standard Launch Vehicle (SLV) 5A, ended successfully in May, 1965, after the fourth launch. All test objectives scheduled for five launches were achieved in four launches, with substantial savings in time and cost."

3C (SLV-5C). The core vehicle plus two segmented strapon solid rocket motors, each of which provides more than one million pounds of thrust (more than two millions pounds combined). Total thrust of the vehicle exceeds 2.5 million pounds. Each solid rocket measures 120 inches in diameter. The pair is attached to the core vehicle as "stage zero" and gives the 3C a 29-mile-high, 3,600-mph head start into space. The first full 3C flight took place June 18, 1965, and the vehicle was acclaimed the nation's mightiest space booster.

The Space and Missile Systems Organization, Air Force Systems Command, manages the program. The industrial team includes the Martin Co. Denver Division, systems integration; Aerojet General Corp., engines for the three liquid-propellant stages of the core vehicle; United Technology Center, a division of United Aircraft Corp., the two 120-inch solid-propellant boosters; and General Motors' AC Spark Plug Division, inertial guidance.

tracking. Plotting the movement of a vehicle through space by use of radar and radio. In the Gemini manned flights, tracking stations around the world followed the craft by skin tracking (radar signal bounce) and by signals from tracking beacons on the Gemini spacecraft.

trajectory. The path traced by a body in flight, as in "lunar trajectory."

Transit (later renamed Navigation Satellite). A U.S. Navy satellite used in an all-weather navigational system. Operational since 1964, the system consists of four satellites in random orbits at altitudes of about 600 miles. The feasibility of the program was shown in 1960 with the launching of Transit 1-B on a Thor-Able-Star from Cape Canaveral with a navigation payload experiment. Another Transit—the 4-A, launched in 1961—was the first to take a nuclear power supply into space. The power unit was a SNAP 3 (Systems for Nuclear Auxiliary Power), a radioisotope-fueled thermoelectric power unit weighing less than five pounds. The Johns Hopkins Applied Physics Laboratory manages the Navigation Satellite program.

translunar injection point. The precise place in an earth-parking orbit at which an upper-stage vehicle must start a spacecraft toward the moon if the mission is to succeed. For example, when an upper-stage Agena D started Lunar Orbiter 1 toward the moon successfully in 1966, the translunar injection point was 119 miles above the earth's surface. The injection point had to be reached at almost precisely the right speed— 24,400 mph; a variation of only 54 mph faster or slower was permissible.

transtage. The upper stage of a Titan 3 launch vehicle. It is designed to restart several times in space, making it possible for the vehicle to change orbits readily and depart from earth orbit into a deep-space trajectory. The liquid-fueled stage provides 16,000 pounds of thrust.

troposphere. "The lower region of the atmosphere, where the average decrease of temperature with altitude is from $5°$ to $10°$ C per kilometer, and the primary vertical transfer of heat is by convection. The troposphere is the seat of weather disturbances. The boundary between the troposphere and the stratosphere, lying at an average altitude of about 12 kilometers [about 7 miles], and at an average temperature of about $200°$ K, is called the tropopause."—(American Institute of Physics)

Tsiolkovsky (or **Ziolkovsky**), **Konstantin E.** A Soviet hero in space flight, who drew scientific and public attention to its possibilities even though he never built a rocket or a space vehicle. The USSR timed the launching of its first Sputnik— Oct. 4, 1957—to coincide with the one hundredth anniversary of his birth.

Tsiolkovsky's contribution was theory, for he formulated data on rocket motion, proposed the use of liquid fuels rather than gunpowder to make large rockets possible, and suggested ways to keep men alive in a spaceship. A teacher of high school mathematics and physics, he wrote his first paper on space flight in 1903, and after World War I wrote a science-fiction novel, *Outside the Earth*. Recognition came to him in the 1920's, when his early writings were republished, and the

USSR celebrated his seventy-fifth birthday in 1932. He died in 1935.

two-gas system. A system in which oxygen and nitrogen, helium, or some other inert gas is used in a manned spacecraft cabin. NASA used a single-gas system operating on oxygen during the Project Mercury and Project Gemini flights, but in 1966 ordered development of a two-gas atmosphere sensor system to be employed for crew health and safety on future flights of from 45 to 120 days. The sensor system will measure the amount of each gas and determine the correct ratio of each for proper control of the cabin pressure. Perkin-Elmer Corp. and SDS Data Systems were assigned development contracts, monitored by the NASA Biotechnology and Human Research Division, Office of Advanced Research and Technology.

USSR scientists reported that their early manned spacecraft used an oxygen-nitrogen mixture. They also disclosed that in 1964 they had conducted a twenty-five-day test with cosmonauts sealed in an oxygen-helium atmosphere.

Tyuratam (called Baikonur in early reports). The principal USSR launching site, from which Yuri A. Gagarin made the first manned flight in 1961. The USSR admitted no Westerner to this equivalent of Cape Kennedy until President Charles de Gaulle of France visited it in 1966. The base is situated in the steppes of Kazakhstan, in Central Asia, and takes its name from the nearest town. Other Soviet space launching sites are at Kapustin Yar, near the Caspian Sea, and Plesetsk, four hundred miles north of Moscow.

ullage. The amount that a fuel tank lacks of being full.

ullage rockets. Small hydrogen-peroxide rockets that fire to keep propellants in proper position during a Centaur upper stage's coasting flight in parking orbit around the earth. Two ullage rockets, each with three pounds of thrust, are used on the Centaur, in which the fuel—liquid hydrogen—is particularly difficult to handle. The ullage rockets exert enough thrust to keep the hydrogen settled in the bottom of the tank, over the pump inlet, so that the main engines have a fuel supply for a restart after about twenty-five minutes of coasting.

umbilical. The cord that links a spacecraft and an astronaut engaged in extravehicular activity (a space walk). The umbilical used by astronaut Richard Gordon of the Gemini 11 crew was thirty feet long. It contained two hoses—one to carry oxygen to the astronaut and the other to transmit nitrogen as fuel for the hand-held maneuvering unit (or space gun). Communications and electric power lines also were in the umbilical. A wrapping of aluminized Mylar protected the hoses from extreme heat and cold, and a sleeve of white nylon encased the umbilical.

unmanned spacecraft. Spacecraft are devices designed to be placed into an orbit about the earth (that is, to become artificial earth satellites) or into a trajectory to another celestial body. By far the majority of devices launched into space are unmanned. Even with no man physically present in the area where a spacecraft is exploring or working, these craft serve as scouts for manned voyages later to the moon, Mars, and Venus; they successfully gather scientific information, and they perform practical work in communications, weather observation, surveying, navigation, and military reconnaissance.

Despite occasional use of the phrase "unmanned program," man plays an essential role in any space program. Dr. Homer E. Newell, who directed NASA's unmanned flights as associate administrator for space science and applications, made this clear when, in 1964, he spoke at the dedication of the Space Flight Operations Facility at the Jet Propulsion Laboratory. Dr. Newell said: "Often in our discussions of the space program we refer to the 'manned program' and the 'unmanned program.' We even talk about manned space science and unmanned space science. Strictly speaking, this is loose talk. There is, in fact, no such thing as unmanned science. Man and this thinking are the prime ingredients of science.

"In the space program, it simply becomes a matter of where the man is in relation to his instruments and measuring devices. For those space missions that we call unmanned, man is back on earth while his eyes and ears and other senses are extended electronically and mechanically far out into space by the spacecraft and its instrumentation. From his remote position, he must monitor, issue commands, receive and record data, make routine or emergency decisions as required in a continuing interchange with his inanimate partner out in space."

The following summary is a brief survey of unmanned exploration and the variety of spacecraft employed for differing missions. The spacecraft families printed in italics in this entry are described in more detail in the alphabetical listing.

LUNAR AND INTERPLANETARY SPACECRAFT

Unmanned spacecraft penetrate lunar and interplanetary space with cameras and an array of instruments. Because they can transmit signals reliably across millions of miles of space, instrumented unmanned spacecraft in the 1960's have increased man's knowledge of interplanetary phenomena in a spectacular way. Millions of items of information have been collected on the solar wind, radiation, cosmic dust, magnetic fields, and other phenomena.

The accomplishments of instrumented spacecraft include those of the *Mariner* family: the first close observation of another planet, Venus, by Mariner 2, in 1962, and the first close-up photographs of Mars, by Mariner 4, in 1965. The Space Science Board of the National Academy of Sciences has recommended Mars and Venus—the planets nearest to earth—as top priority objectives for unmanned exploration in the 1970's (along with a detailed investigation of the surface of the moon). To make future missions possible, NASA is developing a Mariner Mars '69 spacecraft and is studying "follow-on" spacecraft for the 1970's.

For planetary missions, the USSR has employed *Venus, Mars,* and *Zond* spacecraft, but the results have not matched those of U.S. spacecraft.

For lunar explorations, the Soviet *Luna* vehicles and the American *Surveyor* and *Lunar Orbiter* vehicles have proved highly successful. The information gathered by these lunar spacecraft in 1966 probably exceeded all data collected about the moon in all of human history. The Luna series was used both for soft landing and for picture-taking from orbit. In contrast, the United States assigned the soft-landing chore to the Surveyor series and the picture-taking mission to the Lunar Orbiter, a flying photographic laboratory.

In a program completed in 1965, the *Ranger* spacecraft made hard landings on the moon, sending back television pictures of the surface before impact. Three Rangers—7, 8, and 9—proved 100 per cent successful and transmitted 17,276 photographs back to earth.

From its inception with Pioneer 1 in 1958, the *Pioneer* series has investigated the interplanetary environment. Pioneer 1 determined the radial extent of the Van Allen radiation region. In 1960, Pioneer 5 made the first measurements of solar flare effects in interplanetary space. In the mid-1960's, the Pioneers evolved into a new series designed to transmit data on solar radiation and other information from distances up to ninety million miles.

SCIENTIFIC SATELLITES

Scientific satellites may also obtain information by orbiting the earth.

OAO, OGO, and *OSO* are orbiting observatories—astronomical, geophysical, and solar. Each constitutes a stable platform above the earth's obscuring atmosphere. In addition, these newer satellites of the mid-1960's are opening new vistas to science because they are able to make dozens of different kinds of experiments on a single mission. They are standard-ized satellites, each with its own basic structure, power supply, telemetry and command systems, attitude control, and thermal control. Space is provided for instruments that vary from mis-sion to mission. The OGO, for example, has so many anten-nas, booms, solar panels, and attitude-control jets projecting from its boxlike main body that it has been likened to an insect in appearance.

Explorer satellites had their beginning with the illustrious 30.8-pound Explorer 1, which in 1958 confirmed the existence of the Van Allen radiation region in space around the earth. The Explorers, whose contours vary greatly according to the mission to be performed, are of three kinds: (1) Astronomy Explorers, (2) Geodetic Explorers, and (3) Interplanetary Explorers, also known as the Interplanetary Monitoring Plat-form (IMP) series. The IMP Explorers measure magnetic fields, cosmic rays, and the solar winds between the earth and the moon. They provide physicists with a new view of how the earth's magnetic field extends into space and becomes dis-tracted by the sun's influence. The IMP series dates from 1963, when Explorer 18 orbited as far out as 23,000 miles and as close to earth as 120 miles.

Pegasus, the name of the winged horse of Greek mythology, was aptly bestowed on three broad-winged satellites launched in 1965 to gather information on the frequency of meteoroids to be encountered in the near-earth environment. As particles collided with wing panels measuring 96 by 14 feet, the pene-trations were registered and reported to earth. These satellites were the largest instrumented satellites developed by NASA.

San Marco (Italy), *Alouette* (Canada), and *Ariel* (United Kingdom) were among the satellites in which NASA joined forces with the international scientific community.

To study the effects of weightlessness and radiation, NASA has scheduled a series of *Biosatellites* to put animals and plants into space.

The Air Force continues to operate its *Discoverer* satellites, but information is now classified. The Discoverer is both military and scientific, and it tests designs for new spacecraft. The Air Force also operates the *Orbiting Vehicle* series and the *Environmental Research Satellite* series.

The USSR's most frequent satellite launch is that of a *Cosmos,* and this military/scientific family marked its two hundredth launch on Jan. 20, 1968. The USSR does not release results of its Cosmos activities. Many Cosmos satellites make polar orbits, which, as in weather observation, afford a complete view of the globe.

Another USSR scientific satellite is the *Electron,* which was launched in pairs twice in 1964 for magnetic-field and radiation region research. One space booster launched each pair. Because their orbits differ, the pairs provide widely separated positions from which measurements can be obtained simultaneously. The USSR also has the *Proton,* a 12-ton satellite that measures high-energy particles.

PRACTICAL OR WORKING SATELLITES

Satellites, often working in groups of two or more, assist the everyday life of the commercial world by improving (1) global communications and (2) weather forecasting—fields in which revolutionary developments got under way in the mid-1960's. Other satellites (3) assure more accurate mapping of the earth, (4) assist in navigation, and (5) maintain military surveillance.

Communications. Satellite communications entered the commercial realm in 1965 when Early Bird was rocketed into a synchronous orbit—in effect, a stationary position (see *synchronous orbit*)—22,300 miles above the Atlantic Ocean. Linking North America and Europe, Early Bird transmitted telephone calls, television, data, and facsimiles. The 85-pound drum-shaped cylinder was the forerunner of the 150-pound satellites, three times as powerful as Early Bird, with which Communications Satellite Corp. (Comsat) will operate a worldwide network. Only three synchronous satellites are needed for a global system.

Earlier U.S. communications satellites included the Army's *Score* and *Courier 1-B,* NASA's *Relay* 1 and 2, and the American Telephone and Telegraph Company's *Telstar* 1 and 2, all active repeaters of received communications and all operating at low or medium altitudes. NASA's *Syncom* 1, 2, and 3 were lofted in 1963 and 1964 as synchronous satellites. They, too, were active repeaters. NASA's *Echo* 1 and 2 belong to a different classification—passive satellites—because they are giant balloons that simply reflect messages beamed from earth.

The USSR entered the communications satellite field in 1965 with its *Molniya* (Lightning) family.

Weather Observation. Satellites have accomplished significant advances in weather observation. Their cameras track hurricanes, of course, but they also supply pictures of the earth's cloud cover, ice floes, and other data essential for more accurate daily weather forecasts. Since 1966, the United States has conducted the world's first operational weather system. It is the TIROS Operational Satellite (TOS) system, made up of the *ESSA* satellites, the successors to ten successful *TIROS* satellites. At heights of about 450 miles, TIROS satellites have kept watch since 1960 on areas where hurricanes and typhoons are born. *Nimbus* satellites represent a second generation that is bigger than TIROS (830 pounds as against 280 pounds). The first Nimbus was launched in 1964.

Surveying. Earth measurements are obtained more precisely through use of surveying or geodetic satellites. The Army's small *SECOR* satellite, the Army–Navy–Air Force *ANNA 1B,* and NASA's *GEOS* and *PAGEOS* engage in geodetic work. PAGEOS differs in that it is a passive satellite —a hundred-foot balloon that reflects sunlight and provides an orbiting point source of light to be photographed. See *geodesy.*

Navigation. The Navy operates a navigation system consisting of orbiting satellites to give position data to submarines, ships, and aircraft. The spacecraft used was originally known as *Transit* and now is simply called Navigation Satellite.

Military. Secrecy surrounds military satellites. The Soviet's use of the name "Cosmos" for both military and scientific satellites helps to shield their spy-in-the-sky military uses. The U.S. Air Force has the *SAMOS,* which flies polar orbits from 100 to 300 miles high—but the Defense Department has maintained secrecy on SAMOS since 1961. The Air Force also operates the *ICBM Alarm,* a newer designation for MIDAS, designed to provide early warning against ballistic missiles. Another special-purpose military satellite is the *Nuclear Detection Satellite* (once called Vela), operated by the Advanced Research Projects Agency of the Department of Defense. The Defense Department in 1966 began a global communications system, the *Initial Defense Communications Satellite* program, as the predecessor to an "advanced" program.

Other Applications. An unusual addition to the array of unmanned spacecraft was NASA's *Applications Technology Satellite* (ATS), the first of which was launched in 1966. The ATS program will investigate technology that cuts across many kinds of space activity. Experiments were scheduled in communications, weather observation, radiation damage, and other problems of technology.

Full listing of spacecraft becomes complex when it includes special research craft (such as the lifting bodies employed in re-entry tests) and vehicles developed for a special undertaking (such as the Snapshot vehicle that carried the SNAP 10-A, the first nuclear reactor to be orbited in space).

Uprated Saturn 1. A launch vehicle initially known as Saturn 1B. See *Saturn.*

Uranus. The planet seventh from the sun, at a mean distance of 1.785 billion miles. Uranus revolves about the sun once every eighty-four years. It is 32,000 miles in diameter and has a volume about sixty-four times that of the earth. It has five satellites.

V-2. The German ballistic missile used against Great Britain in the blitz of 1944 and 1945, and the forerunner of today's launch vehicles. The V-2 followed a path like an artillery shell and was far more difficult to shoot down than Germany's V-1, or buzz bomb, which was a pilotless aircraft. The United States used captured V-2's to begin development of its own ballistic missiles after World War II.

VAB. See *Vertical Assembly Building.*

Van Allen radiation. Natural radiation in space surrounding the earth, beginning at an altitude of about 600 miles.

The existence of this radiation was confirmed in 1958 by Explorer 1, which carried an experiment designed by Dr. James A. Van Allen, a physicist at the State University of Iowa. Later that year, Pioneer 3 discovered what was called the second Van Allen belt. By the mid-1960's some knowledgeable publications wrote about "Van Allen belts" and others regarded the radiation area as a single belt made up of overlapping layers of protons and electrons. An Air Force manual noted that the "definition of size and shape of these belts depends on selection of an arbitrary standard of radiation intensity and the predominant particle component."

The outer limits were calculated at from 20,000 to 30,000 miles. General indications were that although the radiation was harmful to instrumented, unmanned spacecraft flying for long periods through the area, astronauts on their way to the moon or planets could pass through the zone without undue hazard.

Vanguard. A pioneering American space project intended to orbit the first man-made object during the International Geophysical Year (IGY). The Soviet Union's Sputnik was orbited first, however, and the USSR gained a big lead in the race for prestige. The launching of three Vanguard satellites by the Navy, in 1958 and 1959, lifted American morale, even though they fell far short of matching the Soviet effort. The launches:

	Launch Date	Weight (lb.)	Orbit (mi.) Perigee—Apogee
Vanguard 1	3-17-58	3.25	402 x 2,449
Vanguard 2	2-17-59	22.0	345 x 2,041
Vanguard 3	9-19-59	100.0	320 x 2,307

Only one of the first eight Vanguard launch attempts succeeded in putting a satellite into orbit, but the success—tiny Vanguard 1—was lofted so high that it was expected to remain in orbit for hundreds of years. As part of the U.S. program for the International Geophysical Year, Vanguard 1 collected geodetic observations that showed the earth to be slightly pear-shaped.

Two of the final three launches scored successes. Vanguard 2, a 20-inch sphere, wobbled so much that its electrical signals transmitted scrambled photographs of cloud cover—but the loudness of the signals demonstrated the future merit of the idea of photographing cloud cover. Vanguard 3, shaped like an ice cream cone, carried instruments to measure solar X rays, space environmental conditions, and the earth's magnetic field.

VECO. See *vernier engine cutoff*.

Vela. See *Nuclear Detection Satellites*.

velocity. A term commonly used as a synonym for speed. Precisely, however, it is a vector quantity that consists of the rate—or speed—and the direction of motion.

Venus (planet). Earth's nearest neighbor among the planets. Venus is the second planet in the solar system, lying between Mercury and the earth. It orbits the sun in only 225 days, and approaches to within 26 million miles of the earth at the closest. Missions to Venus can be undertaken during a month-long period occurring every nineteen months.

Venus is very nearly the size of the earth: its diameter is 7,610 miles; the earth's diameter is 7,927 miles.

A constant cloud cover obscures the surface of Venus, and

our knowledge of the planet is scant. The first relatively close-up observations of Venus were obtained Dec. 14, 1962, when Mariner 2 flew within 21,648 miles of the planet. Instruments aboard the spacecraft indicated that the planet's surface may be as hot as 800° F. However, both American and Soviet scientists have advanced theories that radio emissions made Venus appear to be far hotter than it really is. Information from Mariner 2 and from earth-based studies indicates that the surface of Venus is like a desert. In the Mariner 2 mission, an unbroken mass of clouds appeared to range from 45 to 60 miles in altitude and the temperature at the base was put at 200°. Scientists have speculated that these clouds are made up of condensed hydrocarbons.

In 1967 two instrumented spacecraft reached Venus only a day apart. On Oct. 18, the USSR's Venus 4 dropped an instrumented capsule that recorded temperature readings from 104° to 536° as it floated slowly to the surface. Soviet scientists reported that the Venusian atmosphere was full of carbon dioxide and had a pressure fifteen times greater than the earth's. On Oct. 19, the American Mariner 5 flew by and tape-recorded atmospheric data for transmission to Jet Propulsion Laboratory scientists.

Venus (spacecraft). A series of unmanned Soviet Venus probes. Venus 3 won a place in space history on Mar. 1, 1966, when it crashed into the planet, becoming the first man-made object ever to touch another planet. However, the probe's communications failed before impact. Venus 2 had passed the planet on Feb. 27, 1966, at a distance of 14,912 miles, and then had gone into orbit around the sun. Venus 1 failed in 1961 when radio contact was lost—but the craft had made a spectacular start with an interplanetary launching from a parking orbit around earth.

Launched on June 12, 1967, the 2,530-pound Venus 4 reached the Venusian atmosphere on Oct. 18. There the spacecraft burned up, but first it dropped an 842-pound instrumented capsule that transmitted temperature readings for 90 minutes as it descended. Transmission ceased at about the time Venus 4 should have touched down.

vernier engine. A small rocket engine or gas nozzle that assists in providing roll and attitude control of a vehicle and in assuring "fine" control of velocity. On an Atlas launch vehicle, two vernier engines are ignited prior to launch and continue to provide thrust for final adjustments of roll, pitch, and yaw even after the three main engines have shut down.

vernier engine cutoff (VECO). The shutting down of the vernier engines on a launch vehicle. In a launching VECO immediately precedes separation of the launch vehicle from its payload.

Vertical Assembly Building (VAB). A 525-foot skyscraper in which four 365-foot Saturn 5 rockets can be assembled simultaneously, mated with an Apollo spacecraft, and checked out before launching. The VAB dominates NASA's Merritt Island launch area Complex 39 at Cape Kennedy, Fla., and ranks as the world's largest building, for its eight acres almost equal the area of the Pentagon and Chicago's Merchandise Mart combined.

Viking. A high-altitude research rocket developed in the 1950's and used as the first stage of the Project Vanguard launch vehicle. The Viking was patterned after the V-2. It was developed by the Naval Research Laboratory and built by the Martin Co.

Von Braun, Wernher. Director of NASA's George C. Marshall Space Flight Center, Huntsville, Ala., and developer of U.S. launch vehicles ranging from the Redstone to Saturn 5. He was born in Wirsitz, Germany, on Mar. 23, 1912. Dr. Von Braun became technical director of Germany's Peenemunde rocket center and headed development of the V-2 ballistic missile. After World War II, he came to the United States with many members of his original team, and he handled high-altitude tests of the V-2 for the Army at White Sands, N.M. In 1950 he joined the Army Ballistic Missile Agency at Redstone Arsenal, in Huntsville. There he guided the development of the Redstone, Jupiter, and—under NASA—the giant Saturn launch vehicles. Jointly with author Willy Ley, he has written *The Exploration of Mars* and other books.

Voskhod. The second generation of USSR spacecraft, bigger than the U.S. Gemini spacecraft of the same era (11,500 pounds as against 7,000 pounds). Voskhods are launched with rockets that American experts believe have about 900,000 pounds of thrust (as compared with 530,000 pounds of thrust

for Gemini's rockets). Voskhods achieve a featherbed landing, the USSR has said, by firing a second retrorocket after
the parachutes have opened. A new control system reportedly
makes it possible to orient the craft even when on the dark
side of the moon, so that seat belts are needed only for liftoff
and re-entry. A new airlock served as the exit point for cosmonaut Aleksei Leonov to take a "space walk" outside of
Voskhod 2.

Vostok. A one-man earth-orbiting spacecraft used in the
USSR's first six manned space missions, and also in unmanned
missions, accumulating a total of more than sixteen hundred
orbits. U.S. authorities acknowledged the Vostok vehicles to
be far larger than U.S. Mercury vehicles of the same era.
Weight was estimated at about five tons. The Vostoks had the
capability of returning to land, rather than requiring recovery
at sea. Cosmonauts in Vostok cabins breathed a mixture of
nitrogen and oxygen while in flight.

Voyager. A NASA unmanned planetary exploration mission to
Mars planned for the 1970's. The agency is considering
launching two identical Voyager spacecraft with a single
Saturn 5 rocket. The craft would orbit Mars and send down
large instrumented capsules to search for evidence of life.
This program, however, failed to gain congressional approval
in the late 1960's, so NASA outlined plans to send smaller
orbiters to Mars in 1971 and 1973.

Z

zero gravity or **zero G.** See *weightlessness.*

zero stage (or **stage zero**). Solid-propellant rockets—operating much like Fourth of July skyrockets—which are strapped on to a liquid-propellant rocket to impart tremendously greater thrust on liftoff. Addition of a zero stage to an existing vehicle increases the payload tremendously. An example is provided by the Uprated Saturn 1 booster, which now has the ability to put 18.5 tons into a 100-nautical-mile earth orbit. But, says Chrysler Space Division, builder of the booster, the adding of four 120-inch solid rockets to the present booster would give it the ability to lift 38.5 tons.

Zond. A Soviet spacecraft for research in interplanetary space. Zond 3 photographed the far side of the moon from a distance of about 6,500 miles in 1965, supplementing photographs taken by Luna 3 in 1959. Zond 2, however, fell far short of Soviet hopes when it ceased transmitting in 1965 on its way to the vicinity of Mars.

SPACE-FLIGHT CHRONOLOGY

1957

Oct. 4: The USSR opened the Space Age by placing Sputnik 1 into orbit as the first man-made satellite. The 184-pound satellite circled the earth every 96.2 minutes at altitudes of from 142 to 588 miles, and stayed aloft until Jan. 4, 1958.

Nov. 3: Sputnik 2, weighing 1,120 pounds, was placed in orbit. Carrying the dog Laika, it was the first inhabited capsule.

1958

Jan. 31: The United States launched its first satellite, Explorer 1. Instruments on board the 30.8-pound satellite confirmed the existence of the theorized Van Allen radiation region.

Oct. 11: Pioneer 1 became the first successful deep-space probe launched by the United States.

1959

Jan. 2: The USSR launched Luna 1, or Mechta, which missed the moon but became the first spacecraft to go into orbit around the sun.

Mar. 3: The United States launched Pioneer 4, which came within 37,300 miles of the moon and then went into orbit around the sun.

Mar. 17: NASA launched Vanguard 1, its first satellite. Geodetic observations by this 3.25-pound satellite showed that the earth is slightly pear-shaped.

May 29: Two monkeys, Abel and Baker, rode a Jupiter vehicle 300 miles into space and were recovered alive 1,500 miles down the Eastern Test Range from Cape Canaveral, Fla.

Sept. 12: Luna 2, bearing the coat of arms of the USSR, became the first spacecraft to hit the moon.

Oct. 4: Luna 3 took the first pictures of the far side of the moon.

1960

Mar. 11: Pioneer 5 was launched for a deep-space probe and established a radio communications record of 22.5 million miles.

Apr. 1: NASA launched its first TIROS weather satellite, opening a new era of meteorological study.

Aug. 12: NASA launched Echo 1, a passive communications satellite, a 100-foot inflated sphere that reflected radio signals beamed at it.

Aug. 19: The USSR's five-ton Sputnik 5 carried two dogs, six mice, and insects into space, and then made a controlled landing.

1961

Jan. 31: Ham, a chimpanzee, was rocketed 155 miles into space in a Mercury capsule and retrieved alive in the Atlantic 420 miles from Cape Canaveral.

Feb. 12: The USSR fired its first Venus probe from orbiting Sputnik 8. It missed Venus.

Mar. 9: Sputnik 9 carried a dog for seventeen orbits and landed safely.

Mar. 25: Sputnik 10 carried another dog and also landed safely.

Apr. 12: Yuri A. Gagarin of the USSR became the first man to orbit the earth when he made a single orbit in Vostok 1.

May 5: Alan B. Shepard, Jr., became the first American to fly in space. A Redstone missile fired his Mercury capsule into a 15-minute, 22-second ballistic flight 116 miles high and 302 miles down the Atlantic.

July 21: Virgil I. Grissom made the second U.S. suborbital flight.

Aug. 6: The USSR launched Vostok 2 and Gherman S. Titov on a seventeen-orbit flight.

Oct. 27: NASA launched the first stage of the Saturn 1 launch vehicle, developing 1.3 million pounds of thrust.

Nov. 29: Enos, a chimpanzee, rode a Mercury spacecraft for two orbits and was recovered near Bermuda.

1962

Feb. 20: John H. Glenn, Jr., orbited the earth three times in a Mercury spacecraft, Friendship 7.

Mar. 7: The first Orbiting Solar Observatory was launched by NASA.

Mar. 16: The USSR launched its first Cosmos scientific satellite.

Apr. 23: Ranger 4, the first U.S. spacecraft to hit the moon, was launched on its three-day flight.

Apr. 26: The first international satellite, Ariel 1, went into orbit.

May 24: M. Scott Carpenter circled the earth three times in another Mercury flight.

July 10: Telstar, the first international communications satellite, rocketed into orbit, and on July 23 it transmitted the first telecast across the Atlantic.

Aug. 11 and 12: The USSR launched Vostoks 3 and 4 and put Andrian G. Nikolayev and Pavel R. Popovich into orbits for a near-rendezvous (four miles apart at one point).

Aug. 27: Mariner 2 began a 109-day, 180-million mile voyage that carried it past Venus on Dec. 14.

Sept. 28: A Canadian satellite, Alouette 1, launched by NASA, achieved orbit and began years of research in the ionosphere.

Oct. 3: Walter M. Schirra, Jr., made the third Mercury orbital flight, completing six orbits.

Dec. 13: NASA launched Relay 1, an active repeater satellite.

1963

May 15: L. Gordon Cooper, Jr., flew twenty-two earth orbits in thirty-four hours in the final Mercury mission.

June 14 and 16: In the USSR's second dual flight, Valeri F. Bykovski and Valentina V. Tereshkova—the latter the first woman astronaut—were orbited in their Vostok spacecraft and approached within three miles of each other.

July 26: Syncom 2, a high-altitude active communications satellite, was launched successfully by NASA; in mid-August it achieved a synchronous orbit over Brazil.

Aug. 21: The Air Force used the Titan 2 for the first time as a space booster.

Nov. 27: Centaur 2 demonstrated for the first time the use of liquid hydrogen as a rocket fuel in space.

Dec. 21: NASA's TIROS 8 carried the first automatic picture transmission system into space.

1964

Jan. 29: First two-stage Saturn 1 lifted into orbit 37,700 pounds, of which nearly 20,000 pounds was payload.

Apr. 14: Project Fire spacecraft was sent 500 miles into space and propelled back into the atmosphere to provide data on re-entry heating of spacecraft returning from the moon.

May 13: Kiwi B-4D reactor was tested successfully in the NASA-Atomic Energy Commission program to develop nuclear propulsion for space missions.

July 20: SERT 1 proved that an ion electric engine can operate successfully in space.

July 31: Ranger 7 took and relayed to earth the first close-up photographs of the moon's surface before crashing into the moon.

Aug. 28: Nimbus 1 took the first night-time cloud-cover photographs from space with an infrared scanner.

Oct. 12: The first multimanned spacecraft, the USSR's Voskhod 1, with an astronaut, a physician, and an engineer aboard, began sixteen orbits.

Nov. 28: Mariner 4 was injected into a trajectory that carried it 325 million miles to the vicinity of Mars on July 14, 1965, whence it sent back to earth the first close-up photographs of Mars.

1965

Mar. 18: USSR Cosmonaut Aleksei Leonov of the Voskhod 2 crew walked in space for ten minutes.

Mar. 23: The two-man Gemini 3 circled the earth three times.

Mar. 24: Ranger 9, last in its series, sent the first live television pictures of the moon before it impacted.

Apr. 6: Early Bird, the first commercial communications satellite, was launched. It went into commercial operation on June 28, linking North America and Europe.

Apr. 23: The USSR launched its first communications satellite, Molniya 1, which transmitted live television within the USSR.

June 3: Edward H. White II of the Gemini 4 crew walked in space for twenty-one minutes.

June 18: The U.S. Air Force launched a Titan 3-C rocket that attained 2.4 million pounds of thrust at liftoff.

July 16: The USSR put into orbit Proton I, an unmanned satellite representing the heaviest payload ever launched—26,-900 pounds.

Aug. 29: Gemini 5 completed an eight-day mission consisting of 120 revolutions.

Dec. 15: Two Gemini spacecraft, 6 and 7, accomplished the first rendezvous in space.

Dec. 18: Frank Borman and James A. Lovell, Jr., of Gemini 7, completed an earth-orbiting mission of 206 revolutions and almost fourteen days, proving that man could stand the rigors of space long enough to go to the moon and back.

1966

Feb. 4: The USSR's Luna 9 landed softly on the moon and transmitted the first pictures directly from the surface.

Feb. 26: The first Apollo spacecraft—the future "moonship" —flew 5,500 miles from Cape Kennedy to the South Atlantic.

Mar. 1: The USSR reported that Venus 3, bearing the Soviet coat of arms, crashed into Venus, becoming the first spacecraft to land on another planet.

Mar. 16: Two spacecraft were joined in space for the first time when Gemini 8 docked with an Agena target vehicle.

June 2: Surveyor 1 landed softly on the moon and sent back excellent close-up photographs.

Nov. 15: Gemini 12 splashed down safely, completing the Gemini project.

Nov. 23: From a distance of twenty-eight miles, Lunar Orbiter 2 took the first close-up photographs of the moon's Crater of Copernicus.

1967

Jan. 27: The three astronauts named as the crew for the first manned Apollo mission died in a flash fire while testing their spacecraft on the launching pad at Cape Kennedy. They were Command Pilot Virgil I. Grissom, a veteran of the second Mercury flight and the first Gemini flight; Senior Pilot Edward H. White II, the first American to walk in space (from Gemini 4), and Pilot Roger B. Chaffee.

Apr. 24: Vladimir M. Komarov, commander of the Soviet spacecraft Soyuz, was killed when the parachute fouled during his re-entry into the atmosphere after orbiting the earth eighteen times.

Aug. 1: The final mission in the highly successful Lunar Orbiter moon-photography program began with the launching of Orbiter 5 from Cape Kennedy.

Oct. 18: The USSR's Venus 4 arrived at Venus and ejected a capsule that, floating to the surface, recorded temperatures up to 536° F.

Oct. 19: Mariner 5 flew by Venus at a distance of 2,554 miles (after a four-month, 217-million-mile flight) and radioed information about the planet's atmosphere and temperature.

Nov. 9: The Saturn 5 "moon rocket," standing 363 feet tall and weighing more than six million pounds, rose majestically from Cape Kennedy and performed almost flawlessly on its maiden flight. Saturn 5 drove an unmanned Apollo spacecraft 11,234 miles high. The Apollo landed in the mid-Pacific and was recovered.

1968

Jan. 7: The last soft-landing Surveyor spacecraft—seventh in the series—was launched, and it reached the moon on Jan. 9, completing another highly successful U.S. space program.

Jan. 22: An unmanned Apollo lunar module, the "moon bug," made a successful first flight when an Uprated Saturn 1 placed it in earth orbit.

SPACE CAREERS

The participation of the United States in space exploration has created hundreds of thousands of jobs. Because the spacecraft, engines, electronic systems, and other components of space exploration are intricate and sophisticated, most of the employment opportunities call for a college education or for a special skill. Engineers, scientists, and technicians make up a high percentage of the employees.

Jobs and Geography. Space-age jobs are available with manufacturers in the aerospace industry (which produces not only spacecraft but also missiles and aircraft), with universities, with independent research agencies, and with U.S. government agencies, including the National Aeronautics and Space Administration, the Air Force, Army, and Navy. Some of the jobs are in research and development laboratories; many others are in factories. About one fourth of the manufacturing force consists of engineers, scientists, and technicians—a far higher percentage than is customary in other manufacturing industries.

About one third of the aerospace jobs are clustered in California. Many others are concentrated in the East—New York, Connecticut, Massachusetts, New Jersey, and Pennsylvania. Other states leading in employment opportunities are Ohio, Maryland, Florida, Alabama, Texas, Missouri, Kansas, and Washington. About 500,000 persons were employed in 1965 in the production of spacecraft and military missiles, and as many were engaged in producing aircraft. In addition, about 150,000 worked in aerospace electronics and about 150,000 in federal jobs in the aerospace field, bringing the total employment for the industry up to about 1,300,000. By 1968 employment was dropping as the government reduced its space spending.

The Openings. This article directs itself to an over-all examination of the engineering, scientific, and technical positions. The aerospace industry also offers administrative, clerical, and related jobs, and plant production jobs, but these are not essentially different from their counterparts in other manufacturing industries.

Engineers contribute to space research through the development of the essential hardware. Their work extends from the initial planning and design to the final manufacture and testing. (Incidentally, some NASA astronauts hold degrees in aeronautical and astronautical engineering.) Engineers normally specialize in particular areas, working on particular items, such as manned space capsules, unmanned satellites, or rockets. In addition, they usually concentrate on a specific field, such as instrumentation, materials, structural design, production methods, or reliability testing. Branches of engineering represented in space work include aerospace, electronics, electrical, nuclear, chemical, industrial, and mechanical.

Scientists include chemists, metallurgists, astronomers, physiologists, and psychologists. Physicists investigate the laws governing the behavior of the physical work and play active parts in such diverse activities as space exploration, electronics, and nuclear energy. Because physicists often apply the theories and methodology of their science to problems originating in other sciences, some become specialists in areas that combine the knowledge of physics and a related science—so that there are specialists in astrophysics (astronomy), biophysics (biology), and geophysics (geology).

Mathematicians contribute to the space effort by translating scientific problems into mathematical terms for solutions by electronic computers. Some mathematicians calculate the orbits of satellites, and others analyze vibrations to determine whether a proposed rocket could hold together in its intended flight.

In general, scientists are called upon to solve new and difficult space problems by bringing to bear logical minds, intellectual curiosity, and imagination.

Technicians assist engineers and scientists in their work. Their ranks include laboratory technicians, research mechanics, electronics technicians, and draftsmen. Technical writers and technical illustrators produce literature describing how to maintain and operate the space hardware. Production planners plan the layout of the machinery, flow of materials, and sequence of manufacturing operations.

Training and Other Qualifications. A college degree is usually required for an engineering or scientific job in the space field. Many positions demand a doctorate.

Undergraduates preparing for professional aerospace work are advised by the U.S. Department of Labor to obtain a solid grounding in the fundamental concepts and basic general areas of engineering and science. Mathematics and physics, which provide a universal scientific language, are considered particularly important. Graduate studies or on-the-job training are appropriate in the more specialized fields. The advice of a college faculty should be sought in drawing up a program of preparation for a space career.

Semiprofessional workers, such as production planners and electronics technicians, often study for two years in a technical institute or a junior college. Others acquire several years of diversified experience on the job.

Income and Opportunities. Professional and technical space workers generally have higher earnings than similar workers in other industries, the U.S. Department of Labor reports. In part, these higher salaries reflect the rapid growth of research and development activities. Because space exploration is tied to government goals for the conquest of space and also to national security, its future hinges to a large extent on government spending. Government estimates envision a moderate increase in jobs in the aerospace industry during the decade ending in 1975. A study of professional-help-wanted advertisements in metropolitan Sunday newspapers in the principal "space states" provides an excellent indicator of the intensity of hiring efforts by the major aerospace employers. NASA reports that it invites inquiries from "scientists and engineers in all disciplines, at all levels," at NASA installations.

For details on special fields and the location of employers, see *NASA, 20th Century Explorer: A Guide to Careers in Aerospace Technology* which may be obtained from the Superintendent of Documents, U.S. Government Printing Office, Washington, D.C. 20402 for seventy-five cents.

FOR MORE INFORMATION

The following is a partial listing of reading matter that gives additional information on various aspects of man's exploration of space.

SPACE FLIGHT

BERGAUST, ERIK, *The Next Fifty Years in Space*. New York, Macmillan, 1963.

CAIDIN, MARTIN, *Wings into Space*. New York, Holt, 1964.

CLARKE, ARTHUR C., *Interplanetary Flight*. New York, Harper, 1960.

EHRICKE, KRAFFT A., *Space Flight*. 3 vol. Princeton, Van Nostrand, 1960, 1962.

FAGET, MAX, *Manned Space Flight*. New York, Holt, 1965.

GLASSTONE, SAMUEL, *Sourcebook on the Space Sciences*. Princeton, Van Nostrand, 1965.

LEY, WILLY, *Harnessing Space*. New York, Macmillan, 1963.
———, *Rockets, Missiles, and Men in Space,* rev. ed. New York, Viking, 1967.

NEWLON, CLARK, *Aerospace Age Dictionary*. New York, Watts, 1965.

ANNUALS

The Americana Annual, an encyclopedia of the events of the year (see Space Exploration), published by Americana Corporation.

U.S. Aircraft, Missiles and Spacecraft, published by National Aerospace Education Council, Washington, D. C.

212

PERIODICALS

Aerospace Technology, published every other Monday by American Aviation Publications, Inc., 1001 Vermont Ave., N.W., Washington, D.C. 20005.

Astronautics and Aeronautics, published monthly by the American Institute of Aeronautics and Astronautics, 1290 Sixth Avenue, New York, N.Y. 10019.

Aviation Week & Space Technology, published weekly by McGraw-Hill Publishing Co., 330 West 42d St., New York, N.Y. 10036.

Sky and Telescope, published monthly by Sky Publishing Corp., Harvard College Observatory, Cambridge, Mass. 02138.

Space Aeronautics, published monthly by Conover-Mast Publications, 205 East 42d St., New York, N.Y. 10017.

ASTRONOMY (TEXTBOOKS)

ABELL, G., *Exploration of the Universe.* New York, Holt, 1964.

BAKER, ROBERT H., *Astronomy,* 8th ed. Princeton, Van Nostrand, 1964.

MCLAUGHLIN, D. E., *Introduction to Astronomy.* Boston, Houghton Mifflin, 1961.

WYATT, S. P., *Principles of Astronomy.* Boston, Allyn & Bacon, 1964.

MISCELLANY

"Space, the New Frontier," educational-informational book by the National Aeronautics and Space Administration, for sale by the Superintendent of Documents, U.S. Government Printing Office, Washington, D.C. 20402; 75 cents.

DATE DUE